THE
INFINITE
HARMONY

THE INFINITE HARMONY

*Musical Structures in
Science and Theology*

MICHAEL HAYES

WEIDENFELD AND NICOLSON
LONDON

Typeset at The Spartan Press Ltd,
Lymington, Hants

Printed in England by Butler & Tanner Ltd,
Frome & London

Weidenfeld & Nicolson
The Orion Publishing Group
Orion House
5 Upper St Martin's Lane
London WC2H 9EA

British Library Cataloguing-in-Publication Data

A catalogue record for this book is available
from the British Library

ISBN 0 297 81450 8

Meditate upon my counsels; love them, follow them;
To the divine virtues will they know how to lead thee.
I swear it by the one who in our hearts engraved
The sacred Tetrad, symbol immense and pure,
Source of Nature and model of the Gods.

Pythagoras, Golden Verses, 24–5

For my family, in particular my partner: Ali and the girls, who have so consistently kept me on my toes; my ever-resourceful mother, who first instilled in me the power of faith; and my late brother Tony, whose spirited and meteoric flight through this world inspired me to reach for the stars.

Contents

Preface

Although this book covers a wide range of subjects, I feel I ought to make clear at the outset that I am not a scholar. The secrets of modern science, for example, such as relativity and quantum mechanics, the constant properties of light and the structure of DNA, or alternatively the philosophies and precepts of the great teachers of old – in the past, such lofty pursuits of the mind could hardly be said to have been pet subjects of mine. Having said that, however, I will admit to having long felt something intrinsically good in what we loosely call 'religious beliefs', a feeling which, I suppose, began here in an English Sunday school and which, in adult life, was further strengthened during numerous and sometimes reckless exploits in the East.

The details of my trips are for the most part irrelevant, the important point about them being that they introduced me to other cultures and creeds whose mores and principles were, over the years, at least superficially absorbed by me. The *I Ching*, the Koran, the tarot, the *Bhagavad-Gita*, mosques, temples, pilgrims, holy shrines – these kinds of things were all part and parcel of the hippie trail to Kathmandu.

So I became aware of, but was never actually hooked, as it were, by any of the great world religions. To me they were all fundamentally sound. Moses, the Buddha, Confucius, Zoroaster, Christ, Mohammed – whenever I chanced to pick up a fragment of something they had reputedly said, it always seemed . . . right somehow.

Something else which impressed me on my travels was the enormous geographical size of these religious territories, and the power of the effect each religious founder has ultimately had upon untold millions of supposedly free-thinking individuals. Long ago I decided that there was very definitely something *supernatural* in all this. Whoever they were, these 'saviours' of mankind, they certainly knew how to make their presences felt.

That's about as far as my contact with religion went. As for the scientific side of this story, I came to that even later still – whilst attending an extramural course in general studies organized by the social sciences department of Leicester University. I can't remember the name of the young female lecturer who first introduced me to DNA, or the genetic code, but the fact that she did so is a significant feature of this story, because it was this particular revelation which was to ultimately set me off on the uncertain and often wearisome road to authorship.

Whilst studying the developmental patterns inherent within the DNA molecule, I suddenly felt that I had seen this genetic code – the so-called biochemical 'blueprint of life' – elsewhere. The image I then had was unmistakably a repeat of something, or things, already seen. I don't mean *déjà vu*. Rather it was something much more tangible. It was all in the numbers. The number of amino acids employed by DNA in the synthesis of protein; the number, sequence and combinations of the chemical bases of which basic amino acids are made. Transposed into the image I had, this information formed a square grid, eight divisions across, eight down, sixty-four in all. Sixty-four, apparently, is the maximum number of ways in which the four nitrogenous bases can combine into special triplet-units called RNA codons, which in turn correspond with the twenty amino acids necessary for the manufacture of proteins and with the two coded instructions for 'start' and 'stop'.

It was actually the number sixty-four which first caught my eye. It reminded me straightaway of the *I Ching*, the old Chinese *Book of Changes*, which has been used for millennia, and by millions, as both an oracle and a bible. The *I Ching* is a compilation of sixty-four six-line signals known as hexagrams, each of which is accompanied by a text. The book is consulted by dividing at random a clutch of stalks. Six separate movements involving a chance division of the stalks provide the values relative to the six lines of any given hexagram.

But concerning DNA, there was more. I read further that, during reproduction, each of these biochemical triplet-units, or RNA codons, effectively links up with another, already existing triplet-unit housed in the original DNA molecule. In other words, DNA, the long, coiled, double helix of genetic information contained within the nuclei of all reproductive cells, is in reality made up from precisely *sixty-four* basic biochemical *hexagrams*.

Needless to say I was astonished by this 'coincidence'. The structure of DNA had been worked out in the 1950s by the two biochemists Francis Crick and James Watson. The Chinese *Book of Changes* was written sometime before 1100 BC by King Wen of the ancient Chou dynasty. Over three thousand years separated these apparently unconnected revelations and yet, incredibly, I saw that there existed between them an undeniable similarity of structure. Was it merely a coincidence?

Personally I couldn't bring myself to believe this to be so. The correspondence between the structure of the DNA–RNA complex and the system of the *I Ching* was too exact. Accordingly, and with time to kill, I set about trying to prove myself right.

I had no set plan for research. I simply accepted on impulse the extraordinary fact that there once lived a monarch in ancient China who was 'in tune', as they say, with the secret of life, and I supposed that if he was, then quite probably others before and behind him will have been also. That is, much as I respected the work of that venerable Chinese sage, I simply did not believe the copyright was his alone. So I looked elsewhere for the selfsame pattern. It was a rewarding search because, as it transpired, I found this symmetry of composition practically everywhere I looked.

However, before I take the reader on what I hope will be an illuminating journey across aeons of time and vast tracts of space, let me return for a moment to the inner structure of DNA. Sixty-four, as we know, is the square of eight – hence the image of the grid I mentioned earlier, with eight divisions across and eight down. Knowing that the system of the *I Ching* was originally constructed from *eight* basic *trigrams*, I wondered if the genetic code might correspond in exactly the same way. At first this did not seem to be a probability. Apart from the obvious fact that eight was the square root of sixty-four – the maximum number of RNA combinations – there was no apparent basic unit of eight upon which I could focus my attention.

Or was there? Surely, I thought, if I looked hard enough and if my assumption was correct, I *should* find eight biochemical 'trigrams' hidden somewhere inside DNA. Evidently my luck was holding out. After a closer look inside the reproductive cell, I discovered that there were indeed fundamental units of *eight* and *three* coexisting in the biochemical processes of genetic development.

As I said earlier, each of the sixty-four possible RNA combinations correspond with the *twenty* amino acids used in the manufacture of living protein, and also with the *two* coded instructions for 'start' and 'stop'. In other words, there are *sixty-four* biochemical signals on the inanimate side of the genetic code, and *twenty-two* signals on the animate side. Each 'inanimate' triplet-codon therefore corresponds with one or another of the twenty-two evolutionary signals at the next, 'animate' amino-acid level of development. Before the significance of the number twenty-two came to me I remember thinking how much better it would suit my theory if the three nitrogenous bases comprising each codon had corresponded with one or another of *twenty-four* signals at the amino-acid stage of evolution. Three eights, twenty-four – what could be simpler?

I think I was, at this time, in a particularly receptive frame of mind, because the answer to the problem wasn't long in coming. Subsequently, I was very soon delving for the first time since my schooldays into the mystical world of the Pythagoreans.

I should explain that, to the Pythagoreans, the number twenty-two, as a symbol, was sacred. This was because, taken as a numerical expression of a key aspect of musical theory (the Pythagoreans studied everything in its relation to music), the number twenty-two represented exactly *three* octaves of *eight* notes apiece. There are, of course, *seven* individual notes in a standard heptatonic scale. The eighth and last note is simply a repetition, on a higher scale, of the first. But it is also the first note of the next scale of seven tones, so only six other notes are needed to complete it. Seven harmonious notes again sound an eighth, which in turn requires only six more notes to complete the third and final scale:

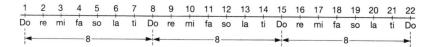

As one can see, viewed in this way twenty-two *is* twenty-four; it represents *three* sets of *eight*.

From this moment on I began to look at the DNA molecule in a very specific light. The *four* nitrogenous bases, the *triplet* RNA codons, the *sixty-four* possible combinations of bases and the *twenty-two* signals at the amino-acid stage of development – all this was beginning to look remarkably like a biochemical manifestation of the heptatonic musical scale.

In the following weeks, as I looked deeper and deeper into the workings of the genetic code, I became convinced that God Himself was a musician. Not only that, in being able to use the inner composition of DNA to draw together the diverse talents of such as Crick and Watson, Pythagoras and King Wen, I began to suspect that, over the centuries, many others have shared the very same conviction.

The rest of this book is based on the assumption that this is indeed the case. A more detailed look at the DNA–RNA complex will be found in the final chapter, by which time I hope the reader, having read all that lies before it, will have come to realize that the modern biochemist has not, in fact, made a startling *new* discovery, but is simply echoing what is, in reality, the oldest song on earth.

CHAPTER ONE

The musical laws of nature

. . . to the great wondrous melodious spirit which covereth
the oneness of us all . . .

> Bob Dylan, *Writings and Drawings*

Observing the world as I now see it – that is, from a musical
perspective – first requires that the reader accept a hypothesis.
Assumed for the sake of argument, the proposition itself has been
intuitively drawn from various sources, all of which will be dealt
with in subsequent chapters. But for the moment I must outline the
theory itself, because only when its basic theme has been understood will it be possible, by reference to both historical and scientific
data, to pinpoint its probable source of origin and so trace, down
through the ages, the extraordinary development of what surely
must be one of the brightest ideas ever to have been conceived. This
idea can be expressed quite simply in the following way:

All phenomena, whether physical or metaphysical, owe their
very existence in space and time to the harmonious interaction of
two fundamental laws of nature.

The first of these laws is the law of triple-creation. This is the basic
law of three forces: of attraction, repulsion and time. According to
this law, within the fundamental make-up of all phenomena there
exists always a passive or negative force (attraction), there is always
an active or positive force (repulsion), and there is always a neutral

1

force (time and all its constituent elements). These three forces manifest within any phenomenon we care to imagine and together combine to generate all of nature's creative processes.

Operative examples of this first law can be found practically everywhere. All matter, for example, is inevitably a conductor of three forces. This fact became apparent when the contents of the atom were finally discovered. The atom consists of a central nucleus containing protons with a positive charge. Negatively charged electron particles describe almost circular orbits at high speed around the nucleus; and these in turn are kept in order by neutron particles, which have no electrical charge. In the subatomic world these constituent parts of the atom are relatively large particles, but as we go further down the scale of matter and energy, we find countless other, even smaller, units of matter which invariably manifest and interact in clearly defined groups of three. This even applies to the smallest particles of matter known to science, the so-called building blocks of the universe, known as quarks, leptons and gluons.

Higher up, so to speak, in the living, or the 'intelligent' world, the same law of three forces is reflected at all levels. Thus all living organisms are composed of three distinctive orders of energy and form: matter in electronic state, matter in molecular state and matter in cellular state. The three combine to generate life: two alone cannot.

On a greater, 'macrocosmic' scale we see the three creative forces effectively controlling the instinctive, almost subconscious divisions of massive populations into tripart allegiances – hence the emergence of first, second and third world nations, upper, middle and lower classes, political right, left and centre, and so on. All these divisions within the higher animal kingdom are *natural*; they are the direct product of nature's first law.

Amid the perpetual motion of an evolving human society, nature's third, 'neutralizing' force can appear in many forms. The third force is, in effect, the 'arbiter' between two, naturally opposing coordinates. A good example of this is the influence of the advisory and conciliatory service at work in the industrial or commercial dispute, or the influence of the ideally impartial judge presiding over prosecution and defence. The same can be said of the part played by the referee in competitive sport, or the role of the agnostic who coexists with the atheist and the believer, or even the concept of money, or profit, which alone makes it possible for today's producers and consumers to interact.

In chemistry the third force manifests itself every time something new is created. Such is the catalyst, whose intermediary properties enable two fundamentally different compounds to fuse into a new and entirely different substance. In electricity, it is the earth connection used to stabilize any given circuit. In medicine, the active doctor attempts to cure the passive patient using the various neutral media of intuition, expertise, drugs and so forth.

The three creative forces are at work everywhere. Nothing is created without them and nothing ever has been, for every phenomenon, without exception, is inevitably a triad of forces, a trinity. A single force, or two forces, can of themselves create nothing. If we observe a definite cessation of movement in anything, this simply means that the third force is lacking, at the given time and in the given place.

Incidentally the terms active, passive and neutral are merely names. In reality all three forces are equally active and manifest as active, passive or neutral only in their relationship one to the others at a given point in time and space. In order of the action of forces they stand in the sequence active–passive–neutral, but by density of matter – because the third force is the conductor of the intermediary principle – the neutralizing force can sometimes be taken to stand between active and passive.

Nature's second fundamental law is the law of seven-part formation and sequence; otherwise known as the law of octaves. To understand the principles of this law it is first necessary to look upon the universe as being an essentially dynamic entity which consists of untold billions of varying vibrations, or 'degrees of resonance'. These degrees of resonance proceed in all kinds and densities of planetary matter. They are generated by the forces controlled by the first law – by triple-creative centres of energy and form – and then they proceed, in every direction, to cross, collide, deflect, increase, decrease, vanish, or whatever. According to the law of octaves, all such degrees of resonance are always inwardly composed and transmute one to another, in seven-fold patterns of formation and sequence.

The effects of the forces controlled by this law are not always easy to identify – particularly in something as dynamic as, for example, a human society. For evidence of their existence we consequently need to look to the measurable world of matter, where phenomena are natural in the fullest sense.

The periodic table of atomic elements in chemistry is the matrix of material creation and will conveniently serve to demonstrate how, in the physical realm at least, the law of octaves is followed to the letter. Formulated on the basis of the atomic number of a given substance, the table begins at its apex with the lightest known element. This is hydrogen, an atom which contains a single electron tracing a specific orbit, or 'period', around its nucleus. The table ends with substances like curium, for example, one of the densest of the elements and more radioactive than uranium or even plutonium. The curium atom plays host to ninety-six electrons which between them trace a total of *seven* periods around the nucleus. No element has yet been found which houses eight circuitary periods.

The periodic table of elements is actually formulated on the overall basis of an *octave squared*. For verification of this and other key facts concerning the nature of matter I shall refer to a remarkable book by the American writer Rodney Collin, *The Theory of Celestial Influence*. According to Collin's view:

> The table of quanta of radiant energy, the table of atomic weights of elements, and the table of molecular weights of compounds do in fact form one single scale, extending from heaven to hell, and on the different rungs of which are to be found every substance knowable and unknowable. (p. 99)

As well as describing in some detail the octave format of the periodic table, Collin explains how the *musical* aspect of the table of quanta of radiant energy (which, having *three* 'primary' wavelengths, is in essence a triple-creative manifestation of energy and form) can be derived from the inner composition of the white ray. The white ray is composed of *seven* fundamental degrees of resonance, known collectively as the spectrum. The ultimate eighth 'note' of this particular 'scale' is of course light itself, the *whole* phenomenon.

In chapter X of his book Collin produces further evidence to suggest that the same principle also applies to the lowest scale of matter, the table of molecular weights of compounds. Although much more complex in structure, organic compounds are seen to obey exactly the same laws as the pure elements. In other words, just as the pure elements are related in seven octaves by their atomic weights, organic compounds are similarly related by their molecular weights.

Common to all of these scales is a relative newcomer to our observable universe – the aforementioned subatomic particle, the stuff of which cosmic rays are made. These minuscule substances permeate the whole of the material world and represent the finest, most rarefied forms of matter in existence. Nowadays newer and ever more obscure particles are being detected all the time, alternating with quantum waves of energy in a kaleidoscope of apparent confusion. Collin's original work unfortunately predates the discovery of particles outside the immediate family of the electron, but had he then been party to information later to be brought to light by modern science, he would possibly have been interested to learn that the nuclear physicist has now found it convenient for his purposes to provisionally categorize all of these subatomic particles into clearly defined divisions, or 'periods', of *eight*.

In a later chapter of the same work Collin details yet another significant musical parallel to be found in nature – that of the physical composition of the body of man. Significantly the endocrinological network of the human organism consists of *eight* fundamental centres of biochemical energy. These various centres, or glands (the pancreas, thyroid, parathyroids, adrenals, posterior pituitary, anterior pituitary, gonads, pineal) function as adaptors or transformers of the general energy created by the human organism. In generating and secreting into the bloodstream numerous salts and hormones, they serve to control and develop many of the physiological and even psychological qualities of the human being. The proportions of these different secretions borne in suspension in the arterial circuit at any given moment make a person what they then are, whether thoughtful, irritated, passionate, lethargic or whatever. Over longer periods, of course, the general condition of the bloodstream

5

must inevitably determine many of the more permanent characteristics of the whole physique.

Interestingly enough, in addition to this basic eightfold biological
network, the human organism also houses *three* distinct but
interpenetrating nervous systems. The cerebrospinal system serves
conscious functions and is connected with the processes involved
with thought; the sympathetic system stimulates unconscious
or instinctive functions and facilitates the processes of sensation; and the parasympathetic and vagus system, in serving to
slow down instinctive functions, is connected in some way with
the neutralizing principle, with emotional functions.

So, just as the endocrine glands and their products reflect the
universal law of octaves, the three nervous systems to which they
are bound reflect the first law, the law of three forces. This
characteristic pattern of the inner structure of the human body is an
exact repetition, in physiological and psychological terms, of the
electromagnetic patterns of energy and form of the white ray of
physics. In other words, in respect of the forces acting through
them, 'man' and the 'white ray' are, objectively speaking, identical
phenomena.

Man, therefore, is an octave of resonance. The white ray is also an
octave of resonance. The universe itself is a fundamental octave of
resonance. So too is the atom and the mountain, the molecule and
the sea, the earth, the oak tree, and the sky. This book even: written
by an octave, with an octave, for an octave . . .

The same applies to each of the three creative forces themselves.
Each one is composed *within* as a fundamental octave of resonance.

This idea of inner resonance can best be explained with the aid
of what is possibly the most easily recognizable of all manifestations of the law of octaves – the seven-tone, or heptatonic, musical
scale.

According to the second law of nature, each of the three creative
forces are themselves subdivisible into seven distinct but interacting orders of energy and form. Taking the first of these forces as
being positive, or active, we may say that it is composed of seven
fundamental aspects or tones. Upon achieving a condition of
optimum resonance these seven tones then combine together to

generate, simultaneously, an *eighth, transcendental* tone. Having thus succeeded the scale of its origin this transcendental signal then becomes the *first* tone of the next scale – the second, negative or passive force. This negative or passive manifestation will also be composed of seven fundamental tones. Upon achieving a condition of optimum resonance this second set of seven tones will also combine together to generate, again simultaneously, a second eighth or transcendental tone, which then becomes the first tone of the next and final scale – the third, neutralizing or mediating force. The completed optimum development of this final set of seven tones results in the simultaneous generation of the third and last transcendental eighth note of the whole series. The given phenomenon is thereby created.

We thus have three successive scales of seven tones each combining harmoniously to produce the completed phenomenon. In other words, the twenty-one successive tones together combine to sound the ultimate twenty-second.

Viewed in this light, any given phenomenon can be described in musical terms as being an outward manifestation of three octaves or resonating energy and form. Or:

1	2	3	4	5	6	7	8	9	10	11	12	13	14	15	16	17	18	19	20	21	22
Do	re	mi	fa	so	la	ti	Do	re	mi	fa	so	la	ti	Do	re	mi	fa	so	la	ti	Do

|←——————ACTIVE——————→|←——————PASSIVE——————→|←——————NEUTRAL——————→|

And relative to its own unique scale or order of existence, the phenomenon so created is in itself a fundamental octave. We thus have twenty-two tones, or notes, of a given triple-octave of energy and form combining to generate seven new notes at the next scale of development:

1	2	3	4	5	6	7	
Do	re	mi	fa	so	la	ti	Do

And these seven new inner notes, in being harmoniously composed, will themselves generate an eighth, transcendental note.

7

```
1  2  3  4  5  6  7  8  9  10 11 12 13 14 15 16 17 18 19 20 21 22
+--+--+--+--+--+--+--+--+--+--+--+--+--+--+--+--+--+--+--+--+--+

              1   2   3   4   5   6   7
              +---+---+---+---+---+---+

                      1
                      +--+
```

So ends the theory. Of course this essentially musical description of creation is by no means a new idea. Long ago the whole concept was very neatly embodied within an ingenious mathematical symbol. This was the formula *pi*, or $\frac{22}{7}$, a formula which is popularly believed to have originated with the Pythagoreans, but which in fact was known as far back as the time of the first dynasties of ancient Egypt.

CHAPTER TWO

Egypt – squaring the circle

As above, so below.

Hermes Trismegistus

The known past of Egypt is the longest recorded by history. Although the Asiatic communities of Mesopotamia go back much further, such societies – typified by the fortress city of Jericho first built around 8000 BC – were localized, autonomous and predominantly tribal. But Egypt was the first organized civilization and, at its peak, produced the first real artists, the first skilled masons and, most significantly of all, the first pyramids.

The date of inauguration of the Egyptian Sothic calendar was 4241 BC. Menes, the first pharaoh, appears sometime around 3315 BC, but it wasn't until the reign of the pharaoh Zoser almost six hundred years later, that the original idea of building in stone for the sake of art was conceived.

Possibly the first real masonic enterprise ever to be undertaken on earth was Zoser's epitaph, the gigantic Step Pyramid and funerary complex at Saqqara. The complex was built by the ingenious architect Imhotep, Zoser's spiritual guide and vizier. Imhotep was ultimately deified for his knowledge of medicine (he was subsequently identified with the Greek god of healing, Asklepios), but it was for his supreme architectual achievements that he was to become known throughout the ancient world as the first true creative genius. This is hardly surprising when one considers what a giant conceptual leap Imhotep had made. To build

9

at this time was not new; but to build for reasons other than practical or material purposes – and on such a monumental scale – represented a remarkably bold step into a new and hitherto unexplored world.

The sophistication of the architecture of the funerary complex at Saqqara is something of a mystery. Why it should be so amazingly advanced in building technique is perhaps a question that will never be satisfactorily answered. Two thousand years before the Greeks introduced the so-called 'Doric' column into their buildings, Imhotep was already deploying elegant ribbed, fluted and papyrus columns with exquisite pendant-leaf capitals. The central tomb was a masterpiece of masonry. It lay at the bottom of a seventy-foot pit hewn out of solid rock, the sepulchral chamber at its base having been fashioned out of huge blocks of granite. The chamber was ultimately sealed off by a perfectly fitting granite plug weighing three tons. On top of the whole structure stood six superimposed terraces all skilfully encased in fine limestone, and the entire complex was surrounded by an enormous enclosure wall measuring 303 by 595 yards – an area a hundred times greater than the old-style brick tomb of Menes at Nagadeh. The monument itself predates by several hundred years the smaller Great Tower of Babylon, which was also a pyramidal structure, but with a rectangular, not a square base, constructed in seven levels of masonry, each being less in area than the one below it.

Given the obvious skill involved, one would have thought that an ambitious architectural project such as the Saqqara complex would have required long experience in the handling of stone, which means that the first pyramid ever constructed on earth was very probably the product of a 'school', of a highly organized and dedicated brotherhood of men with a common, unselfish aim and a not-so-common, extremely gifted master. And they created, between them, the first ever edificial expression of *symmetry*. Thus was the initial die cast, giving birth to a tradition which, in a matter of one hundred or so years, was to develop into the greatest and most influential architectural order the world has ever known.

At Giza, on a rocky plateau, stand the three pyramids of the Old Kingdom dynasties which ranked among the wonders of the ancient world. They were allegedly built by Cheops, Chephren and Mycerinus. Each of these towering man-made mountains is of course a 'wonder' in itself, but it is the Great Pyramid of Cheops of the IV dynasty to which our attention must inevitably turn. The reason for this – a long-disputed fact which I shall verify further on – is simply that this first and only remaining of the seven wonders of the ancient world, be it a tomb, a temple of initiation, an astronomical observatory or whatever, is nothing if not a colossal embodiment in stone of the formula *pi*, of the principles behind the subtle, all-pervading laws of triple-creation and seven-part formation and sequence acted out in nature's every move.

The established view of the Great Pyramid of Cheops is that it was built to function as a tomb and nothing more. That there exists no real empirical evidence to support this theory is a detail which the archaeologist has tended to brush aside, but the fact is that there is no record of any corpse, mummified or otherwise, ever having been found in the so-called 'sepulchral', or 'King's', chamber. Later pyramids certainly were tombs. The mummy and coffin of Mycerinus have been found, in the sarcophagus in the central underground chamber of the third Giza pyramid, with his name and titles on it. This pyramid, however, as with the one built by Mycerinus's predecessor, Chephren, has no internal system of passages and chambers, thus indicating that the succeeding generations of Egyptian masons were in fact ignorant of the Great Pyramid's unique interior design and construction. The second and third Giza pyramids were evidently built merely in imitation of the first, the interior layout of which was kept a closely guarded secret, even from the pharaoh's own son.

When it was finally discovered by the Caliph Abdullah Al Mamun in the ninth century AD, the 'sepulchral chamber' of the grandest 'tomb' of them all was in fact completely empty. If it had been otherwise, we should expect to find some mention of it in Arabic records, but apart from one tale of secret chambers containing priceless treasures and mysterious alien artefacts, there is no evidence to suggest that Al Mamun found even the slightest trace of an authentic artefact, or of any funerary paraphernalia, anywhere in the Great Pyramid. Furthermore, if the chambers had been previously looted, the plunderers must have passed through a hitherto undiscovered network of passages to the 'treasure', because the Arabs had been forced to smash a previously un-touched granite plug in order to gain entrance into the first ascending passage. To then further suggest that these same ghost-like and irreverent 'grave-robbers' also had something of a penchant for old bones and bandages seems hardly tenable. Al Mamun himself is said to have had a cache of gold secreted in the Pyramid in order to pacify his frustrated workmen, who had toiled for months in a spirit of great expectation, only to find the coffer in the King's Chamber not only empty, but even lidless, a bare, rectangular chest carved from a single block of solid granite.

Of all man-made monuments in existence, the Great Pyramid is possibly the most baffling and controversial. Al Mamun himself offered no rational explanation for its unique form and structure, nor as to the reason why the so-called sarcophagus contained no trace of a mummy. Ever since he successfully quarried through to the Great Pyramid's internal system of passages and chambers, numerous travellers, self-educated pyramidologists and archaeo-logists have entered therein and tried to make some kind of sense of it all. Perhaps not surprisingly – given the obvious fact that the structure is wholly geometrical – the main focus of attention has been directed toward the measuring of its dimensions.

The unit of measure most commonly used by the main pro-tagonists in this architectural detective story are the 'pyramid inch' and the 'sacred cubit'. The Egyptian cubit was allegedly employed in the construction of the Ark, the Tabernacle and the Temple of Solomon. Its length was calculated by Isaac Newton to be about twenty-five British inches. Later estimates have put it nearer to 25.025 British inches, which means that the sacred, or pyramid, inch would be about one-thousandth more than the standard British measure, or 1.001 British inches. (According to one pyramid-ologist, a Royal Engineer called Colonel Garnier, the cubit itself can be accurately determined from a 'designed eccentricity' in the Queen's Chamber, where a niche has been sunk into the wall exactly one sacred cubit off-centre.)

The question as to whether these units of measure are valid has long been the subject of much heated debate. But in fact, when considering the ratios and proportions of the structural dimen-sions, the precise values of the units of measure are not what count. That is, provided they are standard units, whether inches, centimetres, cubits or metres, the proportions themselves will remain constant.

In 1926, an Englishman, D. Davidson, published a lengthy volume, *Great Pyramid: Its Divine Message*, the central theme being that the internal system of passages and chambers, indicated to the scale of one pyramid inch to a solar year, embodied a prophetic history of the world, starting in 4000 BC and ending around AD 2045. Modern historians are almost universally contemptuous of the theory of prophetic chronology (indeed all of the alternative theorists are considered to be cranks, 'pyramidiots'), but the key questions raised by Davidson concerning the archaeologists' 'tomb' theory have yet to be satisfactorily answered.

To begin with he notes that both the King's Chamber and the Queen's Chamber were each provided with ventilation shafts, two to each chamber. Clearly there was no need for these during construction and they are of little use to mummies – hence Davidson's not unreasonable suggestion that perhaps the shafts were incorporated specifically for the future, when the Great Pyramid should be studied and measured by the people of a later civilization. He further argues that the tomb theory fails to explain the different peculiarities of each passage. Why, for example, should the seven-coursed Grand Gallery be the height of a two-storey house? Why should it be exactly seven times higher than the first ascending passage, higher even than any of the chambers to which it leads? Why were the means of access to the Grand Gallery and the King's and Queen's Chambers made so small that entrance can only be gained by crouching down in a cramped and awkward position?

In the National Geographic publication *Mysteries of the Ancient World*, the American writer Tom Melham says of the adjoining passages:

> Always less than four feet high, never equipped with stairs or even handrails, usually angled at precisely 26½ degrees, these cramped and slippery corridors make extremely awkward thoroughfares. To walk here is to assume a crab-like crouch and to scrabble slowly through the darkness, focussing on a distant square of light that is the tunnel's end. (p. 72)

Cheops's remains supposedly were transported along this same route, with the attendants doubled over by the passage's impractical proportions, carrying burning torches as they struggled to haul their dead king's funerary sledge up and along the smooth, slippery, slanted floors. As Melham rightly points out, this is a scene that hardly fits in with the solemn and dignified air of Egyptian funerary ritual.

The first ascending passage leads from the entrance at the descending passage into all the inner halls and chambers. It was sealed by a tightly fitting granite plug at its lower end. Archaeologists believe that this plug was retained loose in the Grand Gallery until the death of the pharaoh. The mummy case is then envisaged as having been unceremoniously dragged up the ascending passage and deposited in the King's Chamber, after which the granite plug was supposedly released and left to slide unaided down 43 yards of passage, from the Grand Gallery into the lower end of the first ascending passage. The plug is still there, sealing the entrance, and access to the passage behind is gained only by means of Al Mamun's quarried opening, excavated around AD 800.

According to Davidson, a structural engineer by profession, it is virtually impossible to slide or even push a block of stone along a passage if the block fits tightly all the way. However smoothly dressed and accurately squared, unless it has a certain amount of clearance all round, the block will inevitably jam in the passage. Even if sufficient clearance had been allowed for – which is not, in fact, the case – the block itself would still have to be guided by narrow, loosely fitting side rollers and manipulated down the shaft using some kind of carefully balanced tackle. No evidence of this kind of procedure has ever been found in any of the Great Pyramid's passages and chambers.

This means, of course, that the granite plug must have been *placed* at the lower end of the ascending passage in the early stages of construction, at the time the core masonry had reached course seventeen, which is the level of the plug. Thenceforward access to the Grand Gallery and the upper chambers was possible during construction only so long as they were not fully roofed over, and this wasn't done until half the Pyramid's bulk and over a third of its height had been laid down. From this we can reasonably assume that the first ascending passage was *not* intended as a direct means

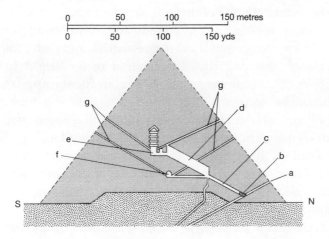

North–south cross-section of the Great Pyramid showing: (a) entrance and descending passage, (b) granite plug and Al Mamun's quarried opening, (c) first ascending passage, (d) Grand Gallery, (e) King's Chamber, (f) Queen's Chamber, (g) ventilation shaft.

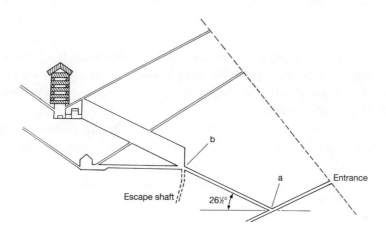

Enlarged view of passages and chambers. Note the steep angle of slope of the passages and the curiously excessive height of the Grand Gallery. The quarried opening (a) to the Grand Gallery entrance (b) is a distance of 43 yards.

of access, not for the builders themselves, nor for any funeral cortege, nor indeed for any of their contemporaries.

Most orthodox scholars of Egyptian history have been reluctant to acknowledge the geometrical/mathematical symmetry of the Great Pyramid, insisting that the relation of its height to the circumference of the base expresses only a coincidental approximation of $\frac{1}{2}$ pi. The accuracy with which this ratio expresses the squaring of the circle is considered to be nothing more than the product of chance. The outer casing stones having long ago been removed to adorn the buildings of what is now modern Cairo, the true external measurements of the structure may never be known, so it is impossible to prove conclusively that it was intended to express the pi relationship.

Colonel Garnier's attempt is based on data taken from the findings of the great pioneering archaeologist W. M. Flinders Petrie. Petrie himself was totally opposed to the idea of intentional mathematical symmetry, but he was the first investigator to make a comprehensive and scientifically accurate survey of the pyramids. According to these findings, the estimated base perimeter of the Great Pyramid is 4 × 9,131.055, or 36,524.22 pyramid inches, which is equivalent to the circumference of a circle whose radius is equal to the monument's estimated height of 5,813 pyramid inches. Obviously we cannot take these measurements as definitive, but from them one can at least say that the mathematical symmetry hypothesis is certainly a possibility. And in fact, within the interior construction, much of which has been preserved sufficiently well to permit extremely accurate measurements, the same mathematical relationship also occurs.

In the 'antechamber' (i.e. the small chamber in between the Grand Gallery and the King's Chamber), there is a granite relief on the wall, distinct from the rest of the masonry, which is 103.033 pyramid inches both in height and in length. Its total area is exactly equal to the area of a circle, the diameter of which would be 116.26 pyramid inches, which also happens to be the exact length of the entire floor of the antechamber:

$$103.033^2 \qquad = \qquad 10,615.79$$

$$\frac{116.26^2 \times pi\,(3.14159)}{4} \qquad = \qquad 10,615.73$$

Incidentally, the length of the antechamber multiplied by *pi* represents the length of a solar year at an inch for a day, i.e. 116.26 × 3.14159 = 365.2412.

Coincidence? Perhaps. The established view is that such proportions are simply nonexistent, the spurious product of over-enthusiastic mathematical juggling.

In his book *The Riddle of the Pyramids*, Dr Kurt Mendelsohn, a former prize-winning physicist who studied under Planck and Einstein, states that the Egyptians of the Old Kingdom had only a rudimentary knowledge of mathematics and that the formula *pi* wasn't known in Egypt even a thousand years after the Great Pyramid was constructed. The pyramid-builders, he insists, discovered the transcendental number *pi* without trying and without knowing.

Although authentic Egyptian records are few (concerning the nature and purpose of the Great Pyramid they are curiously nonexistent), there is, nonetheless, one key piece of nonpyramidal evidence which suggests that this was probably not the case, that in actual fact the Egyptians were definitely aware of the formula precisely at the time of construction of the Cheops Pyramid. The evidence in question appears in the form of a decree, one of the most important administrative documents of the Old Kingdom, which appoints the high priest and vizier Shemaj Director of Upper (southern) Egypt. This document officially places all *twenty-two nomes* (districts) under his authority, enumerating them from first to last. Some time later the pharaoh appoints to the post of deputy (or herald) of his father, the vizier ...j, who seems to be the son of the same Shemaj. But then comes the most interesting part of this ancient injunction, that which states that the son's jurisdiction, as deputy, extends to only *seven nomes*. The symbolism is obvious: father over son, twenty-two over seven. We thus have what is, in effect, a living embodiment of music, in action, in time: *pi*.

As far as the main structure of the Great Pyramid is concerned, there can be little doubt in the minds of any who have contemplated the astonishing masonic precision involved that its creator was no ordinary artisan. Whoever he was, he had something of vital importance to say to the world, and he did rather more than just shout it from the rooftops. The Great Pyramid was originally about 490 feet high. Its base covers an area of more than thirteen acres, an area sufficient, so it is said, to accommodate the combined bulks of Westminster Abbey, St Paul's, and the cathedrals of Milan, Florence and St Peter's in Rome. The whole structure contains a staggering two million, three hundred thousand blocks of limestone, each averaging two-and-a-half tons in weight. Some of the larger granite blocks featured in the interior weigh as much as seventy tons, and the completed building was originally sheathed from top to bottom in an eight-foot-thick exterior limestone casing set with joints measuring a mere fraction of a millimetre wide. Even the most cautious Egyptologist, though he may vehemently deny some of the more startling claims made as to the origin and true purpose of the Pyramid, will readily agree that the level of craftsmanship and expertise achieved by its creators has never been truly equalled in any succeeding age, including our own.

And yet, strangely enough, of the architect who allegedly built it, little is known. His name was Hemiunu, vizier and chief adviser to the Pharaoh Cheops. According to oral traditions reported by the Greek historian Herodotus, one hundred thousand men laboured for twenty years on the project. Whether this is an accurate assessment or not, it would certainly have taken an army of men a good many years to complete, so one would reasonably expect the chief architect of the whole venture to have left behind him a large following of masonic devotees. But this was not the case. For some inexplicable reason Hemiunu did not follow his illustrious predecessor Imhotep up into the hallowed realms of the Egyptian pantheon. In fact, there is no mention of him even having been made a hero of the times, let alone a god. His king also, although clearly a great leader and a brilliant administrator, seems to have left very little of his considerable presence behind. Herodotus has a story that Cheops and his son Chephren, who apparently frequently quarrelled between themselves, were actually hated in their own day. Perhaps this is true. The kind of totalitarian theocracy capable of accomplishing the mammoth task of constructing the Great Pyramid must certainly have been ruthless and unbending to a considerable degree – particularly toward dissenters, who may possibly have regarded their supremely powerful god-king as something of an egomaniac.

Nevertheless, it does seem to be a rather peculiar twist of fate that Hemiunu and his king should subsequently occupy no permanent place in the celestial palace of the great Egyptian divinities. It is true that Cheops himself was a 'god-king' – in possibly the most powerful of all the dynasties – but in subsequent years he and his adviser were very soon forgotten, their tombs defiled and their once-mighty empire steeped in anarchy.

One can't help but wonder why this should be so. Nowhere in the vast annals of Egyptian history is there to be found a more dramatic decline in influence after the death of a great pharaoh. There is a story of later times which relates how Cheops one day summoned his high priest and demanded answers to questions of an esoteric nature. Clearly the pharaoh has no idea of what is really going on, for he quizzes the priest (not Hemiunu apparently) in the manner and tone of a mere novice. It is a contradictory picture to say the least, hardly the kind one would expect to see of the creator of such an important cultural and religious monument as the Great Pyramid. The story suggests, in fact, that the then King of Egypt and his administrative second-in-command might not themselves have been the true guardians of the Egyptian Way but, rather, uninitiated figureheads, the unwitting patrons of a building project, the true nature of which actually lay beyond their ken.

We have already established the likelihood of there having been a school or a masonic order behind this sudden and mysterious upsurge in pyramid-building. And the existence of a school suggests, of course, that there must also have existed a leader or master. So if Cheops and Hemiunu personally had no lasting words of wisdom to say on such an important matter and were in reality unaware of the Pyramid's real significance, then perhaps we should look elsewhere for the true identity of the individual responsible.

Obviously we shall never be able to pin down this enigmatic genius with indisputable historical data. Ancient history is far too tangled a web of fact and myth to permit anything more than a fleeting glimpse into its furthermost reaches. But we began this investigation with an idea, a theory. We then pinpointed the probable origin of this theory as being the canon of proportions embodied within the Great Pyramid, the supreme symbol of the highest masonic order of Egypt. Surely then, it is here, in the legendary school, where the real founding father of Revelation is to be found.

It is at this point where fact, legend and mythology fuse into an allusion, a brief, intuitive glimpse into the mind of a true genius. If in due course we find we cannot put a face to the name, this need not really concern us. It is enough to know that such an individual actually did exist. We have physical proof of that in the form of the Great Pyramid itself, so the fact that we now have to delve into legend for its creator's identity is of no real import to the original purpose of this inquiry.

The ancient Egyptians believed that all true knowledge was derived from the revelations, or 'divine words', which the gods let fall from their lips for the instruction of men. Greek chroniclers, who have provided us with our most reliable sources of information concerning the teachings of the Egyptian priests of the latter-day, Ptolemaic dynasties, held that the so-called exact sciences (medicine, chemistry, astronomy, etc.) had first originated in Egypt under the auspices of a certain individual who went by the curious name of Hermes Trismegistus.

To the Egyptians, Hermes was a god. He was ibis-headed Thoth, the first saviour incarnate, founder of the fabled school for the 'sons of kings', scribe of the gods, inventor of 'writing', and patron of all the sacred arts, including medicine, astronomy, magic and alchemy. The Greek name for this mysterious character, 'Hermes the Great, the Great', became the epithet 'Trismegistus' ('Thrice-Greatest'), and represents a development from the Egyptian 'AA AA', which is found as an epithet of Thoth in late hieroglyphic.

As most of the literature relating to Hermes belongs to the post-Christian era, scholars in general doubt that he ever existed. But of course someone, at some time, conceived of the Great Pyramid, so no matter by what name he was then known, the fact remains that there *was* a legendary Egyptian founder of magic who revealed to man nature's innermost secret. The name given to Thoth by the early Greeks, 'Thrice-Greatest Hermes', is particularly significant in that it is symbolic of the first law embodied within the formula *pi* – the law of three forces. This indicates that Thoth himself was held to have been a divine embodiment of the 'Holy Trinity', or the fully resonant triple-octave, of which one of the first recorded expressions was the old Egyptian triad of the gods: Osiris, Isis and Horus.

The Great Pyramid is associated with the numerological figure known as the Magic Square of Mercury, the number 2080, the sum of all the numbers from one to sixty-four. Mercury was later identified by the Greeks with Hermes, and sixty-four is the numerological equivalent of an octave squared. The special relevance of this particular number is to be discussed later.

Hermes is also associated with what is generally considered in esoteric circles to be one of the most celebrated of all magical texts, the mysterious 'Emerald Tablet', upon which was inscribed the principal hermetic dictum: 'As above, so below'.

As the reader will subsequently see, this all-important message has been echoed many times over and in every age, and is one to which I shall be referring in practically every chapter of this book. Its most significant feature is that it is directly applicable to the musical aspect of the formula *pi*, in that the twenty-two notes designated *above* correspond exactly with the seven notes *below*, with a difference only in scale. This same idea was put forward in the opening chapter, in which I drew a comparison between, on the one hand, the biological make-up of the human organism and, on the other, the physical structure of the material world itself. The human body houses *three* nervous systems and *eight* different centres of biochemical production, and the spectrum of light is composed of *three* primary colours and *eight* fundamental wavelengths, so although they are very different in form, in respect of the forces acting through them man and the white ray could be conceived of as being the same. 'Above' is the macrocosm, of which the sun and the speed of its light are our major conceptual points of reference; 'below' is the microcosm – man himself – who receives impressions at the speed of light, a virtual mirror image of the cosmos above.

In point of fact, it is this fundamental message – that is, the knowledge of the existence of a direct, measurable link between man and the wider forces of nature – which the once-sacred formula *pi* has been conveying to mankind for almost five thousand years.

I should explain at this point that 'classical *pi*', or $\frac{22}{7}$, is really only a close, though workable, approximation of the true diameter-to-circumference ratio of the circle. Whereas classical *pi* computes as 3.142857142857 ad infinitum, 'mathematical *pi*' is nearer to the

3.14159 given earlier, when we were 'juggling' with the Great Pyramid's estimated general dimensions. Within the framework of the theory outlined in this book, however, it is classical *pi* which plays the major part. The later mathematical version is simply a derivative of the original formula and might not have been so readily discovered in the first place had not the classical version been revealed beforehand.

The important point about classical *pi* then, is that its distinctive inner symmetry reflects man's true position in the cosmic scheme of things. Man – and woman, of course – is a 'triple-octave', a composite scale of vibrations which, upon achieving for itself a condition of 'optimum resonance', has the power to strike a single new 'note' up into an infinitely greater, macrocosmic scale. Remember, 'As above, so below'.

With regard to the later, mathematical derivative of the formula, it is perhaps no coincidence that it, too, should have special properties. In practical mathematics, for example, *pi* is designated as a *transcendental* number, which can in turn be used to reconcile the two most fundamental coordinates of geometry: the square and the circle. Curiously its precise value is unknown (it is an irrational, incommensurable number and so may never be computed exactly), but its myriad properties and varied modes of application make the formula itself quite unique. The late mathematician and Fellow of Trinity College, Cambridge, W. Rouse Ball, once quoted a distinguished professor as having said that he found it impossible to conceive of a universe in which *pi* should not exist.

Certainly our own world, or at least the lives of human beings within it, would be very different now had the original, classical version never come to light. Indeed, from the time it was first revealed it has always stood at the very forefront of so-called 'intelligent' thought. Over several thousands of years, in fact, the twenty-two fundamental 'signals' which go to make up the formula *pi* have consisently blended in, or *harmonized*, completely with the entire spectrum of man's intellectual activity. This means, of course, that the concept itself is in every way psychologically whole, which is presumably why it is capable of existing and flowing through the consciousness of subjective man completely independently of time or circumstance. Many religions speak of an 'immaculate conception', a point of absolute perfection at which everything comes to fruition. Such, in a sense, is *pi*; otherwise known as the Sacred Constant, it is a perfect metaphysical creation which, having been immaculately conceived, invariably enters the spheres of human consciousness in a fully harmonious way. One might go even further, in fact, and suggest that evolutionary consciousness itself actually feeds on these mysterious 'hermetic' data; they are its life, its sustenance, and without their existence over the millennia practically all of man's finer thoughts and aspirations should amount to nothing. Consider astro- or nuclear physics, for example, or geometry or mathematics – certainly without *pi* these modern, 'refined' disciplines of the human intellect would have remained little more than intellectual corpses, totally devoid of depth, inflexible to the point of uselessness. Similarly the basic octave matrix underlying both visual art and audible music is the very lifeblood of a vast range of higher emotional experience – as in the spectrum of colour blended to near perfection by the world's great painters (arguably the greatest being the Renaissance masters, who are known to have employed the old Egyptian 'canon of proportions' when creating images of the human body, so that it was divided into twenty-one separate parts), or the seven-tone musical scale with which thousands of gifted composers have fashioned their numerous and much-loved orchestral masterpieces. Clearly this unending stream of creative activity would never have been possible had not the artists themselves possessed intimate knowledge of the form and structure of the octave: the primary component of the immaculate formula *pi*.

So in reality, hermetic influences are omnipresent, they are everywhere, and civilized man simply cannot function without them. Expressed by the ancients through the concept of the Sacred Constant – the key to the 'immaculate conception' – and by later thinkers through the proportions of the most original of all mathematical conventions, these twenty-two fundamental 'signals' comprising what I have chosen to call the 'hermetic code', are a constant metaphysical force, and collectively they represent the final product, the ultimate 'note', if you will, of a completed, fully resonant triple-octave of earthly activity. They are the transcendental manifestations of the superhuman labours of the first recorded master of Revelation. They are the 'signals of Thoth'. They are his spirit.

Those with an eye for history will understand that civilizations, no matter how great and powerful they become, must eventually pass over and die. Existing records show that Egypt's lasted for an incredible three thousand years before it finally perished, a fact which makes it by far the longest-living social system of all time. Obviously such a powerful civilization could never disappear completely without trace so, even though we acknowledge the fact that the Egyptian way of life ended at a certain period in history, this is certainly not to say that its influence died with it. As one civilization expires, or 'decomposes', another is born from it, is inspired by it, and so carries with it some of the more endearing traditions and characteristics of the former. Threads of influence are spun between other cultures, ideas flow, wealth is transferred and, as history unfolds, so new characters, new national identities appear on the scene. This is precisely how we all came to be what we are now, the result of an ongoing process which is still in motion at this very moment.

In spite of the lessons of history, it is difficult for many people today to contemplate the demise of our own civilization. There seems to be a general feeling that modern man, armed as he is to the teeth with his great arsenal of technological gadgetry, is practically unstoppable. Sadly only a small minority of individuals are presently seriously questioning our future – as is evidenced from the lack of response from the more powerful economic states when challenged over ecological issues – but if one considers the potential dangers inherent in, for example, a free-for-all thermonuclear age, together with the growing problems of diminishing ozone, deple- tion of the rainforests and global warming, then the question of our ultimate survival must remain. After all, three thousand years is a very long time when you're barely three centuries old.

Unlike modern man, however, the ancient Egyptians saw the eventual 'decomposition' of their own empire as inevitable. This is why their most important architectural project had to be carried out on such a monumental scale. Clearly the Great Pyramid was built to last, sealed at the time of its construction by a massive, virtually immovable granite plug; and this was done simply in order to ensure that, whether Egypt as a civilization existed or not, its central theme should echo unceasingly across time.

Obviously those involved in the organization of such a prolonged and sophisticated esoteric enterprise lived for nothing else. It was quite literally a life's work. Indeed the very kernel of the philosophy of these mysterious ancient builders – the hermetic code itself – represented, in fact, a complete mode of being, a clear and precise musical system of conduct and development through which it was considered possible to harmonize oneself with the constant forces of nature and so transcend to another, greater world (or scale) beyond. And in fact, this, in a very real sense, is exactly what the father of Egyptian metaphysics has ultimately succeeded in doing – witness the imperishable evidence he left behind him as he journeyed purposefully along the line of time. Working together for several generations, and in perfect harmony, he and his followers created the largest, most intricate stone monument ever to have been built on this earth; and still it stands to this day, its unchanging message radiating constantly to every corner of the civilized world.

To the ancient Egyptians, festivals and religious occasions were of special importance, possibly the greatest of which was the annual re-enactment of the mysteries of Osiris at the sacred city of Abydos. These mysteries were first given publicly under the pharaohs of the XII dynasty, but are believed to date right back to the original Osirian myths of the Old Kingdom. Significantly they were cast in the form of an eight-act drama, an essentially octave format, which many years later was to re-emerge as the model of the most famous Passion Play of all time. I shall be dealing with the Christian phenomenon in a later chapter; however, suffice it to say at this point that these ancient Osirian mysteries, in being of pure hermetic origin, contain all of the key ingredients of the authentic 'Passion'. Thus the familiar cycle of life (active), death (passive), resurrection (neutral) and transcendental 'enthronement' of Osiris is identical in every way to the well-known story of Jesus Christ's tumultuous passage across the world stage.

In fact, the symbol of the octave, and the basic assertion that the universe and everything in it is simply 'crystallized music', lay at the root of all the earliest Egyptian myths.

Hermopolitan theology, for example, which came into being at Hermopolis, the seat of Thoth himself, was one of the most influential theological systems of the Old Kingdom. The myth embraces a pantheon of eight gods, four male, four female, all of whom were said to have appeared simultaneously on the primeval hillock known as the Island of Flame. Because of this system the city of Hermopolis was called, in Egyptian, 'the (city) of the eight' (Khmoun).

Exactly the same format appears in another major theological system formulated about the time of the III dynasty by Memphite priests. According to the Shabaka Stone, a slab of basalt carved at the command of the XXV dynasty pharaoh, King Shabaka, the demiurge or maker of the universe manifested his creativity through the intermediary of eight forms, 'which existed in him'. This was Ptah, the god of Memphis, who by his thought and speech alone created everything that is.

The third and last major myth of the Old Kingdom was the Heliopolitan system, which differs from the two already mentioned in that the gods of its pantheon were nine in number. According to it, the head of the pantheon, the god Atum, alone and unaided, succeeded in fertilizing himself to produce the first of four divine couples. Thus from Atum, the 'Whole', emerged an octave, a series of eight.

Precisely how this early mythological music was made, and what special relevance the number nine, or the ennead – group of nine – has in relation to the octave will be explained in some detail later on.

As we shall see, there are many other quite distinct musical parallels to be drawn from practically every religion and in every succeeding age. In the following chapters, which for the most part have been devoted to examining each of these parallels in turn, there is evidence to show that, once revealed, this original hermetic principle of 'acting out' *musical* sequences of conduct in space and time actually became the *raison d'être* of the whole of evolutionary mankind.

CHAPTER THREE

The bow in the cloud

And seven priests shall bear before the ark seven
trumpets of rams' horns: and the seventh day ye shall
compass the city seven times, and the priests shall blow
with the trumpets.

Joshua 6.4

Roughly thirteen hundred years after the completion of the Great
Pyramid, Moses departed Egypt with the Israelites. Although well
into her inevitable decline, Egypt would still at this time have been
the most powerful and influential civilization of the then-known
world, so it would seem likely that the mass exodus of the Jews was
to a large extent expedited by certain of the conflicting factions of
latter-day Egyptian society.

The Old Testament scriptures have their roots in Jewish oral
traditions dating back to around the time of Moses, a period
roughly coinciding with the emergence of the Vedic civilization of
the Indian subcontinent, and of the pre-Confucian Classical
civilization of the Far East and China. It is generally agreed that the
Old Testament was compiled by various Yahwist and Elohist
writers between 950 and 450 BC. This was long after Moses carried
the original creed out of Egypt. However, all of these writers were
drawing from strong oral traditions and, as they themselves have
attributed the original authorship of certain texts to their prophet,
in the interests of expediency I have decided to rely on their
informed judgement and do likewise.

Even in Moses' day, the Great Pyramid would still have been standing encased in its original outer shell comprised of hundreds of thousands of sheets of highly polished white limestone. Fitted with optical precision and with a finish as smooth as glass, this limestone casing – most of which was still intact at the time of the Arab conquest – would have given the Pyramid a futuristic, almost twenty-first century appearance. One can barely imagine the spectacular sight which must have greeted the early travellers on their approach to the Giza plain. There would have been the majestic Sphinx, reclining in all its former glory, gazing silently out across the northern Delta. It is now believed that this mythical beast could be used as a geodetic marker to indicate the equinox, and once had between its paws an obelisk whose shadow was used to compute the circumference of the earth and the variance in the degree of latitude. Regally poised, with its man-like face set for all eternity, this mysterious guardian of the Egyptian Way must have had a tremendous effect upon every man – even upon the uninitiated, pre-Christian 'pagan'. And, of course, there would have been the colossal Pyramid: one half of an immense, pure white octahedron anchored to the desert, its four mirror-like sides sweeping up under the glare of the hot Egyptian sun like a mountain of fire.

Despite the gradual decline of Egypt's material wealth and power, this enigmatic monument would still have been one of the most impressive of the wonders of the ancient world. Certainly the fact that it exists at all makes it the exception among the seven wonders themselves, because the other six have long since perished, leaving all but the resilient Pyramid half-buried amid the jumbled ruins of legend and myth. Even today it is still a unique phenomenon. Practically everyone who has studied its internal structure agrees that, using only the tools and methods employed by the ancient Egyptians, a precise reconstruction of that ingenious masonic embodiment of nature's two all-embracing laws – astronomically and geographically aligned to the nth degree – would be incomparably difficult to accomplish. It was then, and indeed possibly still is, the most perfect work of objective art ever conceived by man.

In the time of Moses, then, this greatest wonder of the earth would almost certainly have been the focal point of all spiritual thought. It was, after all, the central core of wisdom of the then-known world, so one would expect to find that the 'signals of Thoth' – the sacred proportions embodied within the Pyramid's form and structure – were unfailingly recognized by Egypt's natural successors.

If we now turn our attention to what might be called the 'transcendental product' of Jewish oral traditions, then we shall see that this is, in fact, precisely the case, because the Old Testament itself is permeated throughout with symbolic interpretations of the law of triple-creation and the law of octaves. Beginning with Genesis, the first book of Moses, we read that God created the universe in six days, and that on the seventh day He rested.

Sun	Mon	Tue	Wed	Thu	Fri	Sat	Sun
Do	re	mi	fa	so	la	ti	Do
1	2	3	4	5	6	7	8/1

The very measure of our week is an original hermetic expression of a fundamental octave of time. Moses says that God worked (or played music) for six days and rested on the seventh – the idea being that, at the seventh stage, the period of 'rest', all thoughts, feelings and deeds enacted over the previous week combine together to generate the transcendental impetus for the eighth day, which is in fact the first day of the forthcoming week.

The whole of creation – including the flow of time – is composed of octaves, and it seems for no other reason was Genesis committed to the written medium than to perpetuate this fundamental truth.

Further on in the book of Genesis we come across what must be one of the most popular legends ever created – that of Noah, his Ark and the Flood. Surely this particular story has at some time captured the imagination of every man, woman and child in the Western world. It is *the* perfect legend, composed from beginning to end of hermetic signals of harmony.

Noah was advised to build an Ark and to seal (or 'pitch') it carefully and deliberately. He was then told to take on board this Ark just seven pairs, male and female, of all the beasts that were 'ritually clean', and two pairs, male and female, of all the beasts that were not clean. Also seven pairs, male and female, of all the birds, and so on. 'For yet seven days,' said the Lord, 'and I will cause it to rain upon the earth . . .' (*Genesis* 7.4). This He apparently did. Subsequently, on the seventeenth day of the seventh month thereafter, the Ark grounded upon the mountains of Ararat.

At this point Noah released a raven, but the bird, instead of returning, continued flying to-and-fro until the waters of the earth had dried up. Noah waited for seven days. He then released a dove, but she came back unable to find land. Noah waited another seven days and, after being released for the second time, the dove came back with a freshly plucked olive leaf in its beak. Noah waited another seven days and released the dove again. She never came back.

Now, whatever else this story of Noah's endeavours is intended to be, it is primarily an ingenious piece of esoteric imagery which presents us with an exact picture of the harmonious progression, through time, of a triple-octave of resonance (resonance in this instance referring to a sequence of human activity).

1	2	3	4	5	6	7	8	9	10	11	12	13	14	15	16	17	18	19	20	21	22
Do	re	mi	fa	so	la	ti	Do	re	mi	fa	so	la	ti	Do	re	mi	fa	so	la	ti	Do
RAVEN							DOVE							DOVE							DOVE

If Noah waited for seven days after releasing the raven, then the dove's first flight would have begun on the eighth day. After this first flight the dove returns with no sign. But at least it returns. A vast improvement upon the raven's earlier display of disloyalty and ingratitude. The dove's second flight also begins on the eighth day, which is the first day of the next 'scale' or week of activity. This time the results are even better. Land is found; a new beginning. The raven, signifying the lowest degrees of resonance, remains where it is, caught up in the endless ebb and flow of its own 'base-scale' of existence. Meanwhile the dove, after being released for the third time, subsequently remains free, transcends to the scale beyond, and thus enters a completely new order of existence.

The whole story is a clear description of a harmoniously composed sequence of human activity. It is a Mosaic rendition of psychological music being played, or 'acted out', along the line of time.

Moses later makes a point of telling us that Noah was, at that time, exactly 601 years old. In terms of centuries this figure is significant, because it actually represents the beginning of the seventh stage in Noah's altogether fruitful life. His personal efforts were here compounded and, just as the Lord of Creation had done before him, the good Noah then enters into a well-earned period of 'rest'. Later God was to say to Noah:

> And I, behold, I establish my covenant with you, and with your seed after you.
>
> *Genesis* 9.9

This sign of the covenant established between God Himself and Noah and his creatures was described thus:

> I do set my bow in the cloud, and it shall be for a token of a covenant between me and the earth.
> And it shall come to pass, when I bring a cloud over the earth, that the bow shall be seen in the cloud.
>
> *Genesis* 9.13–15

This sign or 'token' between God and Noah was of course light itself, symbolized by the seven fundamental colours of the rainbow.

Noah's whole life then, in having been righteously conducted (or 'harmoniously composed'), can itself be expressed diagrammatically as a fundamental octave of earthly existence:

```
   1   2   3   4   5   6   7    . . . . . (centuries)
  +---+---+---+---+---+---+---+
   Do  re  mi  fa  so  la  ti  Do
```

So through his own individual effort the Ark-builder had succeeded in developing up to and beyond the stage of evolution designated on this *cosmic* scale by the note 'la', whereupon God then showed Noah the covenant existing between Himself and the earth – at the cosmic (or evolutionary) note 'ti'.

From this essentially musical representation of Noah's life, we see that, at the time of his birth, he is designated by the note 'Do', but that the Creator Himself is also designated by the note 'Do', with a difference only in scale. Now remember that the Lord also said to Noah:

. . . for in the image of God made he man.

Genesis 9.6

As above. In other words, in respect of the natural forces acting through them, man and the white ray (God's covenant) are identical phenomena, they are made in the same image.

Another story from Genesis, almost as popular and well loved as that of the Deluge myth, is the tale of Joseph who, having been sold as a slave by his jealous brothers, subsequently won favour at the court of the pharaoh by accurately interpreting his dreams. Like the legend of the Flood, the story of Joseph is permeated throughout with the symbolism of octaves. Seven lean cows devouring seven fat ones, seven withered ears of corn devouring seven ripe ones. This was the content of dreams which greatly troubled the pharaoh and which Joseph correctly interpreted as being a portent of potential disaster. The resultant story of Egypt's seven years of plenty followed by seven years of famine is well known, and is one which probably has its origins in an earlier Egyptian legend of famine and disaster which followed seven successive low Niles.

Many of these popular legends somehow seem to capture the imagination of everyone. The story of the warrior Joshua is another example. Joshua is credited with having defeated the old fortress city of Jericho by instructing his army to act out a sequence of events strictly in accordance with the principles embodied within the hermetic creed. He was instructed by his spiritual guide to march around the city with all his fighting men, making a circuit of it once for six days running. Seven priests were to walk in front of the Ark of the Covenant, each carrying a trumpet made from a ram's horn. On the seventh day they were to march around the city seven times, with the priests blowing their trumpets. At the first blast of the ram's horns the whole army was to 'raise a great shout', at which, Joshua was assured, the walls of the city would miraculously collapse. According to legend, the walls did in fact 'come tumbling down'.

Whether or not this story should be taken as historical fact we shall possibly never know. But what we do know for certain is that to these ancient people the number seven was sacred. We know also that, if the priests ever did blow on their trumpets, and if each of these in turn sounded out one of the successive notes in an harmonious octave of resonance, then sounded together they would have produced an eighth, transcendental note.

Assuming these same principles can also be applied to well-composed literature, then this essentially harmonic tale of the fall of Jericho would be just such a phenomenon. That is, the whole story of Joshua is *itself* the eighth, transcendental 'note', the psychologically harmonious product of an extremely well-thought-out piece of literary artistry composed and transmitted by genuine adepts. And in fact this famous legend – like the others just mentioned – has actually spanned three thousand years to reach us today, so it can be said with some certainty that the adjective 'transcendental', when applied to this kind of literary phenomenon, describes what is, in fact, a living reality.

In the Book of Exodus we read how Moses introduced the rituals of the Passover and of the Sabbath into the lives of his people. Many new directives were issued at this time and, upon close examination, all of them are seen to be of pure hermetic origin. In fact the whole of Mosaic law appears to have been purposefully introduced into the lives of the Israelites simply in order to instil into them the objective value of recognizing and 'living out' temporal and spatial octaves of harmonious formation and sequence.

Using the Exodus itself as a basis for remembering their natural destiny, the Jews were instructed to treat the Passover as a sacred ritual, to perform it, or act it out, with the utmost sincerity and reverence.

> Thou shalt keep the feast of unleavened bread: thou shalt eat unleavened bread seven days, as I commanded thee . . .
>
> *Exodus* 23.15

And on remembering the Sabbath:

> Six days shall work be done, but on the seventh there shall be to you an holy day, a sabbath of rest to the Lord: whosoever doeth work therein shall be put to death.
>
> *Exodus* 35.2

Concerning the sacred covenant, the Book of Exodus states that Moses was instructed thus:

> Write down these words, for after the tenor of these words I have made a covenant with thee and with Israel.
>
> *Exodus* 34.27

After which Moses stays with his unearthly mentor for 'forty days and forty nights' of intense deliberation; and then:

> And he wrote upon the tables the words of the covenant, the ten commandments.
>
> *Exodus* 34.28

The writer must now indulge in a little intuitive speculation. The Ten Commandments were allegedly written down on two tables, or tablets, which Moses apparently carried down from the mountain. The words inscribed upon these tablets represented the sacred covenant existing between God and the Israelites; and were later to be housed in a gold-inlaid chest or Ark.

The special relevance of the number *ten* is possibly the most significant of all hermetic revelations. We shall later examine why this should be so. For the present I shall simply suggest that, in the meaning of the original text the famous 'Ten' were, in literal fact, *words* and not, as popularly believed, commandments. The Ten Commandments themselves could possibly have been a later embellishment of Mosaic law intended to control and guide a pre-eminently 'lawless' tribe of itinerant Jews as they battled with the elements through their forty tumultuous years of homelessness. But the significant point to be made here is that the covenant itself was composed of ten distinct words, or 'signs', which together combined, somehow, to define or describe the Holy of Holies.

A later description of Moses' ascent up Mount Sinai is also significant. A cloud is said to have covered the mountain for six days and then on the seventh day God called to Moses out of the cloud. Here we are reminded once more of the spectrum of light, of the rainbow symbolizing Noah's pact with his Lord.

The text goes on to relate how Moses entered the cloud and went up the mountain, where he was given detailed instructions on how to make the Tabernacle, or 'Tent of the Presence' (a kind of portable temple), the Ark itself, and numerous other symbolic items. The Ark was described as a chest made of acacia wood. Inlaid with pure gold inside and out, this was to be the vessel for the words, the 'tokens' of the covenant. Around and above the Ark was to be fashioned a cover of pure gold, at each end of which was to be placed a golden cherub with wings outspread. There was also a table to be made, again of acacia wood and inlaid with gold, as well as gold dishes and saucers, flagons and bowls for the drink offerings, and so on.

The instructions for making the lampstand known as the menorah are of particular interest. Also made of gold, the menorah was to have six branches springing from it – three either side. Hanging off each of the six branches were to be placed three cups, each shaped like orange blossoms with calyx and petals. On the main stem or branch (the seventh) were to be placed four cups, again shaped like orange blossoms. A total of seven lamps were to adorn the stand. The menorah was, in fact, hermetically designed from top to bottom. There are twenty-two cups in all. The clutch of four cups attached to the main stem corresponds with the number of base-notes (the number of 'Do's') in a twenty-two note triple-octave. The six sets of three cups attached to the subordinate branches correspond with the remaining eighteen notes. The total number of cups combined together represent the whole phenomenon, which at the next 'scale of resonance' generates a transcendental signal, represented in this instance by the seven major notes of an octave of light.

So the menorah is simply a symbolic expression of the most sacred formula of all. It is *pi*, or $\frac{22}{7}$, the key to absolute unity and perfection. The candelabrum itself, which is still used to this day by millions of Moses' spiritual heirs, is a perfect, harmoniously composed symbol. When all seven of its candles are ablaze with light over the festival of the Passover the individual is confronted face-to-face with a living, vibrant expression of nature's true intent. It is a perfect means by which the absolute musical unity of everything can be remembered. A complete and harmonious octave of light, it is in fact art of the very highest order.

The all-powerful influence which Moses wrought over his

people, and which he has subsequently exercised over the minds and the hearts of Jews, Christians and Muslims alike, marks him out as one of the most influential figures in human history. Clearly a man of no ordinary cast, whose literary contributions bear all the hallmarks of the genuine adept, Moses was a man very much 'in tune' with the original precepts of Thoth. He was a *revelationist*, a chosen individual with a single objective in mind: the transmission of signals of harmony across the space-time continuum. When he finally led his people out of Egypt he took with him the secret plans for the Tabernacle and for the Ark itself, in which was to be enshrined the kernel of the Jewish faith, the 'hermetically sealed' vehicle of intuition and enlightenment embodied within the tripart, sevenfold matrix of the remarkable formula *pi*.

> Verily my sabbaths ye shall keep: for it is a sign between me and you throughout your generations; that ye may know that I am the Lord that doth sanctify you . . .
> Six days may work be done; but in the seventh is the sabbath of rest, holy to the Lord . . .
> It is a sign between me and the children of Israel forever: for in six days the Lord made heaven and earth, and on the seventh day he rested and was refreshed . . .
>
> *Exodus* 31.13, 15, 17

And the Sabbath, in representing the seventh, restful or 'passive' stage in a fundamental octave of time, was the cosmic note 'ti'.

Solomon was the second king of the united nations of Israel and Judea. After succeeding his father, the musician and psalm-writer David, he reigned supreme for forty years. It was in every sense a fortunate reign. His marriage to the daughter of a pharaoh kept him closely allied with Egypt, so it seems highly probable that the King of Israel's connections were with the highest authority of that once-great civilization.

According to Old Testament texts – principally the Book of Kings – Solomon was a passionate builder. That is, he was a mystic architect; and his most famous work – the Temple – was destined to become the very centre and inspiration of Israel's life and devotion. The Temple was to be the next chosen home for the Holy of Holies, a new and permanent embodiment of the esoteric principles at the root of the hermetic creed and, in keeping with the traditions laid down by the founding father of the Egyptian sciences, its originator was subsequently to become known as: 'Solomon the Wise, Solomon the Magnificent, Solomon the Builder of Temples'. Thrice-great: a true initiate. Accordingly one finds that the Old Testament texts depict Solomon as having conducted himself along the line of time in strict accordance with the harmonic sequence of the octave: a living embodiment, so to speak, of real music in action.

The Book of Kings states that Solomon began building the Temple in the 480th year after the Exodus. Evidently this was no arbitrary choice of number. If we take this time-span of 480 years to be forty-eight decades, we can set it out in a musical format like so:

```
        7      14      21      28      35      42      49      . . . . . (decades)
  Do     re     mi     fa     so     la     ti     Do
  +------+------+------+------+------+------+------+
  Do     Do     Do     Do     Do     Do     Do     Do
   1      2      3      4      5      6      7
```

We therefore have one fundamental octave of time consisting of forty-nine decades, and seven subordinate, or 'inner' octaves of seven decades apiece. So Solomon in fact began his hermetic career at the end of the sixth decade in the seventh subordinate octave of time, at the point designated by the seventh 'inner' note – the cosmic (or metaphysical) note 'ti'.

We are further informed that this point in time represented the *fourth* year of Solomon's reign and that the Temple complex took precisely seven years to complete. The symbolism of the number seven here needs no explanation, but the fact that he began building in the *fourth* year of his reign is also significant because, if we examine once more the musical format of the formula *pi*, we see that it contains exactly four base-notes:

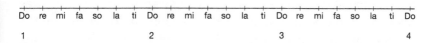

```
+--+--+--+--+--+--+--+--+--+--+--+--+--+--+--+--+--+--+--+--+--+
Do re mi fa so la ti Do re mi fa so la ti Do re mi fa so la ti Do

1                    2                    3                    4
```

These four fundamental base-notes designate the preparatory stage of development of any given evolutionary phenomenon. At least the first three do. The fourth is the transcendental product of the union of the three. As we know from earlier discussion, when the first three distinct orders of energy and form 'resonate at optimum frequencies', they then generate a signal which transcends to the greater scale above. In Solomon's case this 'greater scale' happened to be the building of the Temple, an enterprise which, not surprisingly, took exactly seven years to accomplish. Incidentally, the periods forty days and forty nights, or forty days/years in the wilderness, mentioned so many times in both Old and New Testament texts, may also have their roots in this principle: that is, in the basic number four. Whenever such temporal formulae are mentioned they appear to denote, like the first four years of Solomon's reign, a preparatory stage of evolutionary development – a 'sound' base, as it were, upon which to build a life.

The seal of Solomon was the six-pointed star, later to be corrupted by Western legend into a 'Druid's foot', or five-pointed pentangle. In musical terms the six-pointed symbol itself represents the unifying interval between the notes 'la' and 'ti' of a composite scale of resonance, but it is also an expression – as with the subordinate branches of the menorah – of the union of *two* sets of *three*; a combination having particular significance in relation to the ten 'words' of the Mosaic covenant and other hermetic revelations. The ramifications of this particular 2×3 combination will be examined in a later chapter.

Continuing for the present with the Book of Kings, we learn further that Solomon's throne – the focal point of the palace complex – had six steps leading up to it. The throne itself marked the next step, the sacred seventh, which meant that the king himself, personified as having attained for himself the ultimate condition of being, represented the transcendental eighth note of the whole hermetic phenomenon, theoretically with power enough to transmit his harmonious influences out to spheres way beyond his own scale of space and time: that is, across millennia.

Built on Mount Zion in Jerusalem, the original Temple became the national shrine and spiritual model of ancient Jewry and was believed to have been situated on the spot where Abraham built the altar for the 'sacrifice' of Isaac. It was destroyed by the Babylonians under Nebuchadnezzar in 586 BC, and the Jews were deported en masse to Babylonia – doubtless taking with them their own particular interpretations of the original hermetic code. Elaborate descriptions of the Temple are to be found in the Book of Kings, although no buildings quite like it have ever been excavated. It was constructed with two courtyards at the front of the shrine after the Egyptian fashion and the interior was lit by latticed windows similar to those in the great Temple of the Sun (Ammon-Ra) at Karnak. Much of the Hebrew work known as the Talmud deals with the ritual of the Temple, which was apparently divided into two spheres. According to tradition the higher sphere, known as the 'sanctuary that is above' was believed to correspond with the lower, or the 'sanctuary that is below' – an idea entirely reminiscent, of course, of that ancient, all-wise dictum of the first master of Egyptian metaphysics: 'As above, so below'.

The main furnishings of the Temple consisted of three major items. First there was the Ark itself, the container of the secrets, representing the one, indivisible whole. Then there was the Mercy Seat, positioned above the Ark, overshadowed by the enormous wings of the two golden Cherubim. Finally there was the Hebraic Menorah, the golden, seven-branched candelabrum, symbolizing, as we now know, the periods between the eight fundamental stages of development, not only of the devotee himself, but of all phenomena.

CHAPTER FOUR

The hymn-singers

The seven great sages, and, before them, the four Manus
are born out of My Mind, and all creatures in these planets
descend from them.

Krishna, the *Bhagavad-Gita*, X, 6

Two thousand years before Christ there was a tremendous up-
heaval in central Asia. The inhabitants – the great Aryan race –
began to migrate in large numbers, west into Europe and east into
Persia and India. Their language was the original source of many of
the later tongues, such as Sanskrit in the East, Persian and
Armenian in Central Asia, and Greek, Teutonic, Italian, Slavonic
and Celtic in Europe. Similarly their religion formed the basis of
numerous others. In Europe its influence all but disappeared,
remaining only in fragments of superstition and legend, but in Asia
it continued to thrive in the form of the Vedic tradition.

The Aryans reached India by way of Persia, spreading from the
Himalayas down into the plains surrounding the Ganges, and
finally forcing their way south of the Vindya mountains into all
parts of the subcontinent. The defeated aboriginal tribes either fled
into the hills and forests, or remained to be treated as serfs so, like
the Egyptian and the later Greek, Vedic society itself was essentially slave-based.

Very little of the pre-Aryan belief system is known today. They
were illiterate and left no records. In Vedic poems they are
frequently denigrated as evil-doers, inferiors and even demons,

but from the customs and languages of the existing tribes descended from them it would appear that they believed in an ill-defined kind of pantheism in which nature was infested with evil spirits, demon lords who had to be appeased by witchcraft and offerings.

Aryan beliefs, on the other hand, were far more uplifting. Their gods were lively and benevolent, with none of the sinister traits of the fiends which struck fear in the heart of the natives.

The Vedic scriptures consist of four main sections. The first section is comprised of the *Four Vedas* – the word *veda* having been derived from the root *vid*, 'to know' – hence, 'knowledge', or 'secret science'. It corresponds with the Latin *videre*, 'to see', and the English, 'to wit'. Compiled between 1500 and 1200 BC, the *Vedas* consist mainly of hymns and vocalized *musical* recitals. The first three – the *Rigveda*, the *Samaveda* and the *Yajurveda* – were known collectively as the *travi-vidya*, or 'threefold body of knowledge', the hymns of which formed a liturgical body that grew up around the cult of the soma ritual. (Soma was a hallucinogenic drink made from the prepared juice of an unspecified plant, possibly the mushroom fly agaric.)

The first *Veda*, the *Rigveda*, contains 1028 hymns. In practice they are chanted in syllabic style, a kind of elevated speech with one syllable to a tone. During recitation three levels of pitch are employed, which are used to emphasize grammatical accents in the texts. In Hindu temples even to this day these basic forms of the *Rigveda* can be heard. The *Rigveda* hymns are the basis for a later collection, the second of the *Vedas* known as the *Samaveda*. This *'veda* of the chants' uses words more as a vehicle for the voice, its hymns being sung in a more florid, melismatic style. The third, the *Yajurveda*, is primarily a collection of prayers addressed to the numerous gods of the Vedic pantheon. To these first three *Vedas* was subsequently added a fourth, the *Atharvaveda*, which is a collection of magic spells and incantations. Being less archaic in both metre and language, the *Atharvaveda* wasn't actually recognized until a later period in Vedic history.

The *Brahmanas*, or *Ritual Treatises*, and the *Aranyakas*, or *Forest Treatises*, taken together comprise the main body of Vedic law, the Aryan equivalent of the Mosaic guidelines adopted by their Near Eastern cousins, with their emphasis on disciplined and harmonious (or rhythmic) conduct. The final section – the *Upanishads* – consists of a series of 240 philosophical texts which deal with the nature of God and the soul and the meaning of existence. They form the root of much of the later Hindu philosophy and even today are respected and studied by all thoughtful Hindus.

Given the sheer volume and depth of the Vedic scriptures, the question must arise as to where such a sophisticated body of knowledge might have sprung from. The Aryans themselves reached India from Central Asia, from the region surrounding the Oxus, and by that time – circa 1500 BC – they had already compounded their musically reinforced disciplines into a definite form of teachings, sacred rituals and dances. On a global scale, of course, the Oxus region is comparatively close to Egypt and, as the Aryans were no mean travellers, it is likely that some of them will have travelled south-west and witnessed the unique spectacle of Giza. In fact, evidence of early contact between the Egyptians and the Aryans is to be found in the fourth section of the Vedic scriptures, the *Upanishads*, the central theme being that there is *one* impersonal reality – Prajapati – of which the *three* greatest gods, Agni, Indra and Varuna, are the names and forms. Varuna later became personalized as the ruler of the universe who guided all the forces of nature, Indra became the god of rain and Agni (Ignis) the benevolent god of fire.

Significantly this so-called 'Vedic' image of the three aspects of one reality corresponds exactly with the original hermetic idea of the eternal 'trinity'. Moreover there are further clear indications which suggest that the originators of Vedic philosophy also recognized the underlying *musical* form of their 'thrice-great' Prajapati. According to tradition, these three separate components of the trinity are verifiable, or supported by Proofs, of which there are considered to be eight distinct types, namely:

1 Pratyaksha Praman – Proof of Perception by direct Conviction
2 Anuman Praman – Proof of Knowledge by Inference preceded by Perception
3 Upman Praman – Proof of Knowledge by Comparison, Resemblance or Similarity
4 Shabdya Praman – Proof of Knowledge by Word
5 Aitihya Praman – Proof of Knowledge by Tradition
6 Arthpatti Praman – Proof of Knowledge by Presumption

7 Sambhav Praman – Proof of Knowledge by Probability
8 Abhav Praman – Proof of Knowledge by Non-existence

The eighth Proof, as one can see, is of a totally different nature from the first seven. It is an 'otherworldly' Proof, and clearly suggests that the eighth stage in this Vedic path to enlightenment is of a supernatural or transcendent nature.

Many of the ideas inspired by the Vedic culture subsequently entered into the later traditions, not only of the Hindus, but also of its Central Asian heirs, the Persian Magi. In due course we shall examine in greater detail some of the myths and legends of the descendants of these early Aryan migrants. Armed with their mysterious 'vid' they forged their way across the Persian plateau some time prior to the Exodus of the Jews, the 'chosen people' who also happened to acquire on their travels a secret body of lore.

In the *Brahmanas*, the first king of India is given as Manu Svayambhu (the Self-born Manu), also known as Manu Prajapati (Manu of the Three Names or Forms). Said to have been born directly of the god Brahma, Manu is depicted as a hermaphrodite. The female part of the king's body ultimately gave birth to two sons and three daughters, from whom was descended a chain of 'Manus'. This myth is clearly of hermetic origin, thus: Brahma (1), Manu the hermaphrodite (2 + 3), first son (4), second son (5), first daughter (6), second daughter (7), third daughter (8). The tenth sage in the succeeding chain is the one who ruled over the earth when the 'great flood' occurred and, like Noah, is said to have built a boat to carry his family through the deluge. This tenth sage – the survivor of the flood – apparently had nine sons, the eldest of which was also a hermaphrodite, from whom arose the two principal lines of royal descent – the 'Solar' dynasty, from King Ila, and the 'Lunar' dynasty, from King Ilā.

The so-called 'metrical *Smrities*' are a collection of extremely ancient texts, some of which – particularly the text known as *Manava Dharmasastra* – are believed to be the inspired words of the very first Manu. Written in Sanskrit, the opening verses of the *Manava Dharmasastra* narrate how the great sages approached Manu and asked him to explain the 'sacred law'. Manu agreed and subsequently gave to them an account of the creation as well as of his own origin from Brahma:

He (the divine Self-existent), desiring to produce beings of many kinds from his own body, first with a thought created the waters, and placed his seed in them.

That (seed) became a golden egg, in brilliancy equal to the sun; in that (egg) he himself was born as Brahma, the progenitor of the whole world . . .

The divine one resided in that egg during a whole year, then he himself by his thought alone divided it into two halves.

And out of these two halves he formed heaven and earth, between them the middle sphere, the eight points of the horizon, and the eternal abode of waters.

The Laws of Manu, 1: 8–9, 12–13

Verses 12 and 13 are of particular interest. Evidently the imagery of a 'heaven', a 'hell' and a middle sphere between is a direct reference to the universal trinity of creation. The eight points of the horizon represent the underlying octave matrix to which the whole adheres.

Reading on we find further evidence to show that the underlying message of the legendary Manu's discourse is of a hermetic nature:

Moreover, the great one, the soul, and all (products) affected by the three qualities, and, in their order, the five organs which perceive the objects of sensation.

But, joining minute particles even of those six, which possess measureless power, with particles of himself, he created all beings.

The Laws of Manu, 1: 15–16

All 'products', including God (the great one) and the (human) soul are affected by the 'three qualities', i.e. by the law of triple-creation. And the six kinds of minute 'particles', when joined together with 'particles' of the Creator Himself, result in the creation of *all* beings. From a hermetic perspective one can see why, of course, because the 'particles' of Brahma himself represent the seventh stage of creation, the cosmic note 'ti'.

Further still the special significance of the number seven is confirmed by Manu himself:

Because those six (kinds of) minute particles, which form the creator's frame, enter (a-sri) these (creatures), therefore the wise call his frame sariri (the body).

That the great elements enter, together with their functions and the mind, through its minute parts the framer of all beings, the imperishable one.

But from the minute body (-framing) particles of these seven very powerful Purashas springs this (world), the perishable from the imperishable.

Among them each succeeding (element) acquires the quality of the preceding one, and whatever place (in the sequence) each of them occupies, even so many qualities it is declared to possess.

The Laws of Manu, 1: 17–20

As we can see, the latter part of this text is a perfect description of the mode of transition of the varying notes (elements) in a seven-tone musical scale – a fact which leads one to suppose that the great Manu Prajapati, whoever else he may have been, was nothing if not an initiated, 'thrice-great' brother of the brotherhood of brotherhoods.

Then I, desiring to produce created beings, performed very difficult austerities, and (thereby) called into existence ten great sages, lords of created beings.

Mariki, Atri, Angiras, Palastya, Pulaha, Kratu, Praketas, Vasishtha, Bhrigu, and Narada.

They created seven other Manus possessing great brilliancy, gods and classes of gods and great sages of measureless power.

The Laws of Manu, 1: 34–6

In this last extract of the text we see once more a direct reference to the fundamental notes of an octave (the seven other Manus). Note also that there is a further reference to the ubiquitous symbol of the *decad* – the 'ten great sages', called into existence by Manu himself (after an intense period of self-development), who between them created an *octave* of great brilliancy. This brings to mind the famous 'ten' of Mosaic tradition, which, as I suggested in an earlier chapter, referred to the innermost secret underlying the sacred covenant existing between God and the Israelites.

A full explanation of this mysterious interconnection between the decad and the octave will be given in a subsequent chapter.

CHAPTER FIVE

The Magus

Zurvan has seven faces, and on each face three eyes . . .
Persian Rivayats, Vol. II, 1.10

The first millennium BC saw the emergence of three great Near Eastern civilizations. The Exodus of the Jews culminated in the occupation of the land known as Israel-Judea; the Babylonians, later captors of the Jews whose Mesopotamian origins date back to the Akkadian times of the third millennium BC, settled around the Rivers Tigris and Euphrates; and the descendants of the Aryan-Vedic migrants – the Persians – occupied the major part of the Iranian plateau.

The Egyptians, of course, were always relatively close to hand. Since the third millennium BC, long before the Babylonian King Hammurabi expounded his legal code, Egyptian metaphysical concepts had been the guiding light of the whole of Central Asia. Whilst ancient Mesopotamian art forms grappled with the stark realism of wars and their aftermaths, of the hunting of beasts and their tortuous death agonies, Egyptian aspirations appeared to have been far more refined. Their funerary art frequently depicted the ordinary events of social existence, suggesting not only an appreciation of the finer things in life, but also, through ritual observance of the Osirian mysteries, a refreshingly optimistic view of life after death.

The Assyrians, the Babylonians and the Sumerians were all on the contrary wholly pessimistic. In general they seem to have

47

believed that mankind had been created by the gods simply in order to serve, and that their reward (of prosperity) extended no further than this life. This kind of dismal view of the afterlife would have been unlikely to have much appeal to the peoples of neighbouring states. Israel at least would have none of it. As we have seen from the activities of Moses and Solomon, the spiritual aspirations of the whole nation were rooted firmly in Egyptian soil.

Persia, the other great nation of Central Asia, was essentially Vedic in origin, but by the sixth century BC the numerous gods of that pantheon had increased in number to the point where the original canon had become lost in an overpopulated netherworld of confusion. In the main, the country itself seems to have been populated by pastoral folk concerned with the breeding of cattle, but who were frequently pillaged by ferocious nomadic tribes. Little is known of their belief system. In early Persian literature there are implications of the existence of some cult, but the gods to whom it was dedicated are unspecified. One of them may well have been Mithra, a powerful god of the Vedic pantheon closely associated with Varuna. Mithraism – the 'bull cult' – later became a religion popular with the Roman forces throughout the empire. Also prominent was a deity known as Zurvan, the ambivalent god of time whose name can be traced back almost to the era of the Exodus. Haoma was another popular god (from the Vedic 'soma') – a personalized deification of the hallucinogenic plant used in religious ritual for centuries before, both in India and in Persia.

This proliferation of new and often obscure deities effectively grounded the original Vedic concept of Prajapati and the eight Proofs. The time for reform had come; and the task of bringing about this reform fell to Zoroaster (or Zarathustra), an attributed member and perhaps originator of the legendary hermetic brotherhood of the Persian Magi. In the later Greek civilization Zoroaster was revered as the father of the esoteric, the archetypal Magus, the great Persian sage. As a measure of his influence upon Greek thought it is worth noting that some of the most powerful minds of the day – including Socrates, Plato and Aristotle – were all known to have respected and familiarized themselves with the traditions of the Magi.

Zoroaster was probably born sometime around 630 BC. The date is uncertain and ever in dispute, but it does nevertheless coincide with the emergence of the first systematized faith of Persia. The tales and legends surrounding Zoroaster's life and work are necessarily timeworn, obscure compilations of mythological symbolism and probable, but unprovable, fact. It is believed that his early ministry, during which he converted a king named Vishtaspa, took place in ancient Chorasmia, the region covering today's western Afghanistan, Khorasan in Iran, and parts of Turkmenistan. Although it is not known exactly where he was born, Zoroaster's materialization into planetary form was held to have been the result of an immaculate conception; and like so many of the great revelationists in history, he was frequently the object of demonic attempts to destroy or seduce him. Legend has it that as a young child he was accosted by a wizard who made an unsuccessful attempt at killing him by crushing his head. Later the forces of evil tried to destroy him by fire; and later still a herd of stampeding oxen would have crushed him to death had not the leading ox miraculously turned to heel to stand guard over him. Further attempts to destroy him were many, and as his influence began to spread he had to contend with the malevolent sorcery and catch-22 polemics of his reactionary Persian elders. Zoroaster apparently survived all these adversities, sometimes with the assistance of divine intervention, at others simply through his capacity to confound the ageing, subjectivized arguments of contemporaries and elders alike with his superior wisdom.

The story of Zoroaster's purported visions is particularly significant and in fact provides us with a clear indication as to the true nature of this 'superior wisdom'. The first is said to have occurred in his thirtieth year (the beginning of his fourth decade). One day whilst fetching water from a river he had a premonition of the vision which was about to befall him. Suddenly he saw before him a colossal transcendent figure, at which point he allegedly left his physical body and was transported into the presence of the angels, where he was instructed in the ways of the Good Religion. This particular vision was reputedly the first in a well-defined and successive series. There occurred in fact a total of eight, each of which was described as having been a transcendental experience through which the prophet saw God and His Good Mind – the eighth and last marking the completion of the revelation and the beginning of the next stage in his hermetic career. Clearly this whole story, like the legend of Noah, is a piece of esoteric imagery describing how Zoroaster, from his thirtieth year, lived or 'acted out' a complete and harmonious octave of activity along the line of time.

The *Gathas* (hymns) of Zoroaster are composed in a traditional style and metre closely resembling that of the *Vedas*. Within them is to be found further indication as to the extent of his knowledge of hermetic principles. He speaks, for example, of seven beings, the Amesha Spentas (Bounteous Immortals), the sons and daughters of God (Ahura Mazda). Greatest of these is the Immortal Good Mind – the entity who greets the soul at death and then accompanies it to heaven. Then follow, in succession, Truth, the Desired Kingdom, Devotion, Immortality, Integrity and Obedience. According to Zoroaster these seven beings are all aspects of the Creator in which the dedicated follower of the Path of Truth is able to share. We shall later return for a closer look at this Persian route to eternity; suffice it to say here that the Bounteous Immortals themselves simply represented states of being, to be developed and attained purposefully and in strict compliance with the principles of music – hence Zoroaster's final inclusion of an eighth transcendent Immortal: Spenta Mainyu, the Bounteous Spirit of Ahura Mazda himself.

According to the Persian myth of 'world creation' and 'world maintenance' or 'renovation', the process of world history is divided into four basic periods, each of which lasts for three thousand years. (Hindu philosophy also reflected this hermetic system of temporal division through the concept of the great aeon, which was composed of four lesser aeons, or *yugas*.) We thus have, according to Persian mythology, four basic temporal triads, each triad being composed of three millennia apiece. From a musical perspective the four periods themselves represent the fundamental base-notes of a triple-octave of time. Each of these major periods is then expressed as being composed within as a triad – 3 × 1000 years, presumably with an active millennium, a passive millennium and a neutral one. Interestingly enough a millennium is a ten-fold unit, a symbol of the decad, to which, it may be remembered, Mosaic law attached such importance. Similarly the inclusion of the decad in this Persian myth of creation also has a special relevance, but one which, along with the Hebraic mystery and numerous others, will not become apparent until a later stage in this investigation.

The first two major periods are said to be concerned with creation. The third is the period when the wills of the Persian gods Ahriman (active force) and Ormazd (passive force) are 'mixed in the world'. Modern scholars view the creation of these two deities as the origin of a misguided dualism. Ormazd and Ahriman – the former radiant with light, the latter dark and destructive – are said to be the two sons of Zurvan, the mighty god of time. It is thought that this Zurvanite myth was designed to explain the relationship of the dual principles of good and evil, but it did so at the cost of turning Ahura Mazda into a subservient deity, i.e. into Ormazd, the passive of the two sons of time. It should be remembered, however, that most of our information about the origin of this myth comes primarily from accounts of Manichaean, Christian and Muslim writers, which means that the 'dualism' in question need not necessarily have been the result of Zoroaster's lack of vision, but rather that of later, uninitiated commentators. Zoroastrianism is in essence a hermetic phenomenon, so the concept of two diametrically opposed deities both subservient to a third is in fact expression of the trinity and nothing more. The fourth and last major period of this Persian myth, which upon completion would be designated in a triple-octave format as the twenty-second and ultimate note, 'Do', is believed to represent the time when evil will be overcome.

Zoroaster further embellished this myth by subdividing the first millennium of the last three-thousand-year period into four subordinate ages. The first was described as the age of gold, the second the age of silver, the third the age of steel, and the fourth the age of iron, a time when evil would combat the forces of nature with renewed vigour, and when the prophet's spirit would return to earth in the form of another great Messiah.

Only fragments of Zoroaster's original practical teachings have reached us today. His major literary contribution – the *Larger Avesta* – was comprised of twenty-one books, known as the *Twenty-One Nasks*, (three sections of seven books apiece). Presumably his intention in adopting this familiar format was to help his followers experience for themselves the all-embracing reality of the musical laws of nature by traversing their very own 'triple-octave' of existence 'in tune', as it were, with the psychological nuances, or 'tones', of the hermetic code itself. The end result of this Zoroastrian process of initiation into the cosmic mysteries would have been the unwritten twenty-second 'Nask', read not by eyes over pages in hours, but felt, experienced, through the transcendental state of enlightenment. The traditional Western twenty-first coming-of-age celebration at which the developing individual is given the 'key to the door' probably has its roots in this very principle.

Though short-lived by, say, Christian or Buddhist standards, Zoroastrianism still managed to sweep supernaturally across the whole of the Persian empire. Above all the other cults and religions of its day, it was *the* one most capable of blending in, or 'harmonizing' with the collective psyche of the entire Persian civilization, remaining prominent until the advent of Islam in the seventh century AD. Its influence can be traced in many of the world's major belief systems, including the Judaic and the Christian, in Greek and Gnostic literature, and in Manichaeism. Even today, some twenty-six hundred years after its original conception, there are millions of Parsees in India for whom a vague semblance of the ancient faith of Persia is still a complete way of life.

Coincidentally Zoroaster is reputed by some to have been one of the teachers of the mathematician and philosopher Pythagoras of Samos, the Greek initiate who ultimately translated the laws of universal harmony into the audible medium of practical music, and into the now familiar mathematical form of the formula *pi* – the very soul of modern science. We shall shortly be examining in some detail the works of the Pythagoreans. The Greeks, as we shall see, were inheritors rather than originators. For the present, however, it will be sufficient to acknowledge the fact that Zoroastrianism itself has played a far greater role in the development of human consciousness than the Western mind is ordinarily wont to believe. As we further progress on our musical journey down through the ages we shall therefore find it necessary to return periodically to some of the more significant of the revelations of this Persian Magus and his Indo–Iranian forebears.

CHAPTER SIX

Eastern variations

And this is the noble truth of the way which leads to the
stopping of sorrow. It is the noble eightfold path.
Samyutta-nikaya, 5: 421

In the later philosophy of the Aryans, which developed during the
time known as the Epic period (circa 600 BC), the Vedic image of the
three aspects of one reality subsequently became transmuted into
the characteristic Hindu idea of creation: the trimurti of Brahma,
Vishnu and Siva.

In Hindu mythology, the fundamental cosmic cycle is the 'day of
Brahma', a period of 4320,000,000 years which is known as a *kalpa*.
At the beginning of this 'day', Vishnu is said to sleep upon the
cobra Shasha, signifying endless time. From Vishnu's navel is born
Brahma, who creates the universe on behalf of Vishnu, who then
awakes and controls the cosmos throughout the day. At the end of
the day the world ends up being destroyed by Siva and is once more
absorbed into Vishnu's body. The god sleeps for a further *kalpa*, the
'night of Brahma', after which the process is repeated more or less
ad infinitum. This, of course, is comparable in every way with the
Zoroastrian version of events, engineered by Zurvan, god of
endless time, and his two sons, Ormazd and Ahriman.

Within the *kalpa* are one thousand smaller cycles, or 'great aeons'.
These are each divided into four lesser aeons, or *yugas*, each of
which is considered to be shorter and less blissful than that which
preceded it. The world is at present in the fourth lesser aeon, the

Kali Yuga, which began in 3102 BC, and which will continue for 400,000 years until Vishnu, in the form of an entity known as the Kalkin, destroys its evil elements, thus paving the way to a new age of gold. Here again one is reminded of Zoroaster's prophecy of a four-fold degeneration in the quality of life on earth, through gold, silver, steel and iron. Thus the figure of the Kalkin, Vishnu's tenth incarnation, corresponds with the return, after ten centuries, of the spirit of Zoroaster.

So the Hindu trimurti of Brahma, Vishnu and Siva is simply a later Aryan description of nature's triple-creative processes first revealed to man by the hermetic order of Egypt. Note also that the present, fourth aeon – the Kali Yuga – is considered as having begun at or about the time when Egypt itself was set to develop into the greatest civilization of the then-known world.

At the beginning of the Epic period two major new influences of thought began to materialize: Buddhism and Jainism. The systemized faith of Jainism was founded by Vardhamana Jnatriputra, a slightly older contemporary of the Buddha. Jnatriputra, in true Vedic tradition, taught that truth was relative to our standpoints and that there were seven different ways of speaking of a thing or its attributes. This all-too-familiar concept was the origin of the old story of the six blind men who each laid hands on a different part of an elephant and tried to ascertain the true nature of the animal. The man who caught the ear thought the creature resembled a winnowing fan; the one who grasped the leg imagined it was a pillar; another clutched at its tail and declared that it was a rope – and so on, but only the seventh man with eyes to see could perceive the nature and form of the whole animal. Jainism thus appears to have been a minor but integral part of the ongoing hermetic phenomenon, another carefully thought-out variation on the original Egyptian theme of 'transcendental evolution' through harmonious conduct.

Originally confined to the Ganges valley, Jaina sects later spread to parts of the north of India, to the south, in the region of Mysore, and to western India, where there are to this day about two to three million practising Jains. The creed itself has not, perhaps, reached out to as many people as the more prominent of the world's religions, but even in the face of the greater influences resulting from the subsequent teachings of the Buddha, it has continued to attract ardent followers through more than twenty-five centuries of time. This fact alone shows that there is very definitely some kind of transcendental power at work here, and it is a power which, as we have seen, can be clearly identified as having been born of a set of concepts which had initially been, as it is so aptly termed, 'hermetically sealed'.

Roughly around the time Zoroastrianism was taking root in Persia, Guatama the Buddha was born into the high-caste Brahmin line of Aryan nobility. A natural Hindu, he was a disciple of the 'twice-born', the initiated Brahmins who effectively controlled and guided the spiritual aspirations of the major part of India.

It has already been established that even at the time of the Buddha's birth the central theme of Egyptian metaphysics – i.e. the hermetic code – was wholly embedded within the collective psyche of the changing Vedic-Epic civilization. By this time, however, the original teachings of Manu had become weakened, 'toned down' through centuries of ordinary human corruption. From a contemplative application of the universal symbols of the triad of the gods and of the eight Proofs thereof, contemporaries of the newly arising Epic tradition would have been expected to realize for themselves the all-embracing unity existing beyond time and dualistic perception, but the confusion caused by the many lesser gods of the Vedic pantheon gradually began to cloud the minds of potential initiates with the stuff of imagination. Evidently this was why the Buddha subsequently implemented his own reforms. Recognizing the need to reorientate the seeker with Hermes' original example of 'living out' a musical existence in time, he introduced a system of self-development known as the Eightfold Path, with its emphasis on 'right living' as the only realizable means of progression up through an ascending or evolutionary scale of existence toward the ultimate goal – the transcendental eighth step/note, *nirvana*.

The underlying pattern of the Buddha's system is unmistakably hermetic in form and structure. First we have the four Noble Truths: the Noble Truth of Pain (or suffering), the Noble Truth of the Cause of Pain, the Noble Truth of the Cessation of Pain and, finally, the Noble Truth of The Path that leads to the Cessation of Pain, which is the Noble Eightfold Path itself.

The four Noble Truths represent a practical expression of the four preparatory base-notes of an evolving triple-octave of 'intelligent resonance':

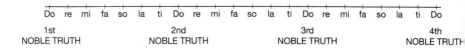

Do re mi fa so la ti	Do re mi fa so la ti	Do re mi fa so la ti	Do
1st NOBLE TRUTH	2nd NOBLE TRUTH	3rd NOBLE TRUTH	4th NOBLE TRUTH

The first three Truths are exactly analogous to the three creative forces of nature and, once realized or assimilated by the evolving entity, together combine to sound the fourth and last base-note, the transcendental twenty-second note of the whole series which, as the fourth Noble Truth implies, marks a new and higher order of existence for the individual: the treading of the Eightfold Path itself. The Path runs thus: Right View, Right Thought, Right Speech, Right Action, Right Livelihood, Right Effort, Right Mindfulness, and finally Right Concentration. Being fundamentally sevenfold in composition (Right View and Right Concentration are essentially the same thing), the Eightfold Path constitutes a practical means by which developing aspirants can harmonize their individual presence with the constant forces of nature:

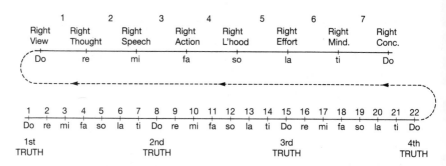

We now have a complete reversal of the mathematical symbol *pi*. That is, $\frac{22}{7}$ has become $\frac{7}{22}$. The significance of this reversal will become clearer in the light of Greek revelation to be examined shortly.

*

The oldest surviving account of Guatama's life was written over eight hundred years after his death, but isolated incidents of his career have been told as parables for millennia, appearing as episodes written in marginal commentaries of ancient texts on Buddhist law. Although there exists a variety of different versions of any given event, it is still possible to compile a generalized picture from those events which are most often told.

The Buddha was a historic figure, the son of an elected chief of the Sakya clan, born in the sixth century before Christ in what is now Nepal. The story proper begins in the year 568 BC, when prior to his conception the Buddha's mother, Queen Maya, had a dream. In this dream four great kings lifted her bed, carried it to the Himalayan peaks and placed her beneath a great Sal tree seven leagues high. She was then escorted to a golden palace at the top of a mountain where, as she reclined in her bed, a white elephant entered, circled her three times, and then touched her right side. Upon hearing of the dream the queen's husband, King Suddhodhana, summoned sixty-four Brahmins to interpret its meaning, whereupon they told him to rejoice, because the queen had conceived a son. Subsequently, after the magical forecast of ten lunar months, the miraculous child was born out of his mother's right side and received in a golden net by four beautiful goddesses.

The first point of interest is that the dream begins with the symbolic number four, a number which, when applied to the musical principle of 'transcendental evolution', represents the preparatory stage (scale) of development, the four base-notes. Queen Maya then ascends to the next stage (scale) of the dream – the seven-league stage symbolized by the height of the Sal tree. And as one might expect, the final stage takes place even higher still, in a golden palace where, after a series of three distinct movements, the dream comes to an end.

The imagery is clear enough. Like Zoroaster, the Buddha was 'immaculately' conceived. In fact the form of symbolism used to describe the queen's dream is a graphic description of the fourfold/eightfold system of self-development subsequently devised by the Buddha himself. Note further that the symbol of the decad also finds a fitting place in the story, and that it culminates in a 'miraculous' event, i.e. the birth of the Buddha. Possibly the Buddha's mother was inspired by the old Vedic legend of the ten great sages of Manu, whose line of descent also culminated in a supernatural happening – the creation of seven other Manus, innumerous gods, sages, and so on.

One final detail to be noted at this point is the number sixty-four, the number of Brahmins called upon by King Suddhodhana to interpret the dream. As with the symbol of the decad, the number sixty-four is one which carries with it a message of special significance in the unchanging language of hermetica. A full explanation is given in the following chapter. Continuing for the present with the story of Buddha:

According to tradition, when still a newborn babe the Buddha rose from his silver cushion and took seven steps in each direction to examine the universe. The symbolism involved here: seven steps taken in the direction of each of the cardinal points is yet further evidence to show that the author of the episode believed in the absolute hermetic conformity of *all* phenomena, for even the universe itself was depicted as being composed of seven 'steps' (or spheres of existence), each being supported by the four 'base-notes' of the compass.

Exactly seven days after Guatama was born, Queen Maya is said to have died. Such a simple statement – and yet the strange fact is that within it is to be found a complete and exact exposition of the whole of hermetic lore. In other words, the entire contents of the first chapter of this present book are here condensed into a single sentence. Active 'birth', passive 'death', and the sevenfold intermediary principle inherent within the flow of time – the trinity and the octave.

Guatama's subsequent renunciation of the trappings of princely life and his eventual departure into the exoteric world of suffering and misery is the stuff of legend, of fairy tales, depicting a realm of existence in which logic has no place and time has no dominion. Such is the mark of the perfect tale: of immense human appeal, harmoniously composed in every way – and, like the legend of Noah, written to last.

The details of the Buddha's victorious entry into the transcendental eighth sphere of existence (*nirvana*) are worth noting. He is said to have sat under the Bodhi tree for forty-nine days, whereupon Mara, the god of evil, who had followed him in vain for six years in the hope of catching him in an unkind or evil act, made, in the seventh year, his final assault. Mara was subsequently defeated, leaving Guatama free to advance to his final three stages of meditation. Enlightenment came after fifty days. Obviously the forty-ninth day marks the end of the seventh week, or note, in a fundamental octave of time. The fiftieth day designates the beginning of the eighth week/note, where the great Buddha finally received his just reward.

An identical version of this evolutionary pattern of development is to be found in the Old Testament Book of Leviticus, in which Moses receives instructions from his mentor on Mount Sinai:

> Six years thou shalt sow thy field, and six years thou shalt prune thy vineyard, and gather in the fruit thereof;
> But in the seventh year shall be a sabbath of rest unto the land, a sabbath for the Lord . . .
> And thou shalt number seven sabbaths of years unto thee, seven times seven years; and the space of the seven sabbaths of years shall be unto thee forty and nine years.
> Then shalt thou cause the trumpet of the jubilee to sound on the tenth day of the seventh month, in the day of atonement shall ye make the trumpet sound throughout all your land.
> And ye shall hallow the fiftieth year, and proclaim liberty throught all the land unto all the inhabitants thereof.
>
> *Leviticus* 25.3–4, 8–10

As with all major religions, the whole science of Buddhism is an extremely subtle and complex body of data. It is not intended to analyse it in detail in this book. The aim has been only to establish the underlying hermetic structure of the doctrine itself, and then to recognize the supernatural influence it has exercised over the life of Aryan man. This overall sway is evidenced by the fact that on the continent of Asia today there are millions upon millions of Buddhist devotees who daily, *constantly*, recognize and follow the harmoniously composed, 'immaculate' precepts of their much-loved and enlightened avatar; and they have been doing this, moreover, for over two and a half thousand years.

CHAPTER SEVEN

Consulting the
I Ching

To know harmony is called the constant;
To know the constant is called discernment.

Lao Tzu, *Tao Te Ching*, LV, 126

Our knowledge of ancient Chinese history is scant and incomplete. Most of the literature relating to it is fragmentary and of uncertain date, so we have only a vague picture of the early development of the first real dynasties. According to traditional historical thought, the seeds of Chinese civilization were sown by a company of legendary heroes known as the Five August Emperors. Certain Taoist traditions state that before the Five August Emperors lived semihuman, semidivine figures sometimes called the Three August Ones. The first of these three – Fu-hsi – is credited with having invented the calendar, marriage, writing, the civil administration system and the famous eight trigrams of the celebrated *I Ching*, or Chinese *Book of Changes*, of which we shall speak later.

The earliest extant collection of historical documents relating to China is the *Shi Ching*, the *Book of History*, reputedly one of the thirteen classics associated with, if not actually compiled by, the great Chinese sage Confucius. The *Book of History* contains references to Chinese culture from the earliest times. According to it, when the last of the Five August Emperors (Emperor Shun) took over from his predecessor (Emperor Yao), he '. . . gave audience to the princes of the east. He set in accord their seasons and months and regulated the days.' Of Emperor Shun it is also said that with only five servants to help him (making six in all), he kept order everywhere under 'Heaven' (the seventh?).

Almost immediately we see an interesting and familiar picture begin to emerge. The Three August Ones and the Five August Emperors, sometimes referred to as the Eight Immortals, are entirely reminiscent of another well-known and superhuman breed of eight demigods – the Zoroastrian Bounteous Immortals. The last in the Chinese pantheon, the Emperor Shun, is followed in fact by another semidivine hero – the earlier-mentioned Yu the Great. Yu is historicized as founder of the old Hsia dynasty (circa 2000 BC) and is generally associated in Chinese legend with a Deluge myth akin to that of the Near East. Presumably Yu is depicted as having survived the Flood because, like Noah, he was the transcendental product of an harmonious octave of earthly activity. Noah and his family (his wife, three sons and their wives) numbered eight, of course, and although his Chinese equivalent is numbered nine in the succession of divines, no stretch of the imagination is required to exact from both legends the selfsame musical message of transcendental evolution. We have already met Yu the Great's divine forbear, Fu-hsi, inventor of the mysterious eight trigrams of the *I Ching*. The *I Ching* itself will be dealt with in some detail at the end of this chapter, but it will be useful to note here that the cumulative symbol of eight trigrams, or tripart 'signals', is a very clear expression of the triple-octave, of *pi*.

Of all teachers in Chinese history, there can be none which match up in stature with the saintly Confucius. For over two thousand years the whole fabric of Chinese society has been woven around the precepts of this one man, so he can justly be regarded as being one of the most influential figures in human history. The modern dictator Mao Tse Tung made great efforts to eradicate all traces of Confucian influence and yet today, barely a decade after the Chairman's demise, one can already see the rigid policies of the present-day administration beginning to slacken once more in favour of age-old traditions.

That Confucianism as a creed, or as a metaphysical 'force', has proved to be so penetrating a phenomenon suggests, above all else, that the precepts upon which it was founded are of a psychologically harmonious nature. They have made more sense to more people than any other body of Oriental law, and one cannot doubt that they will continue to do so long after the bedraggled contents of the Chairman's little red book have been dissected and returned to their numerous sources of origin. As with the effects of Zoroastrianism, and of Buddhism and Judaism, the question once again arises: where did this extreme psychological potency come from? The answer of course, as before, is that it came, not directly from Confucius himself, but from emissaries from Egypt. There is in fact ample evidence to suggest that this is the case.

The orthodox version of the life of Confucius is of questionable historical accuracy but, as with the story of Guatama the Buddha, it is possible to paint a generalized picture from those stories about him which are most often told. His name was K'ung-tze, although he became known throughout China as K'ung Fu-tzu (K'ung meaning 'Master' or 'Sage'). Born in 551 BC in the feudal state of Lu in Shantung province, Confucius lived in comparatively humble circumstances, but his clan was of noble ancestry from the royal house of Shang (1766–1122 BC). From an early age he showed a keen interest in history, ritual and especially music and as a young man held a minor public position as a liturgist functioning at funerals and other ritual gatherings. In his early twenties he became a teacher of philosophy, ethics and history, attracting a circle of ardent disciples, many of whom remained with him until his death. The next thirty years were spent developing the principles of ideal human relationships and 'right living', which were to form the basis of Confucian philosophy.

Confucius was friendly with a ruling prince of Lu, to whom he acted as adviser, and in middle life was given the post of magistrate of the city of Chang-tu. It was here that he first put his theories of 'right government' into practice – much to the benefit of the citizens under his charge. His patron subsequently died and the new ruler of Lu for some reason rejected his advice, treating him in such an offhand way that Confucius decided to quit his home and set out on a journey through the neighbouring states. He thus joined the familiar ranks of wanderers and scholars who at that time made their living travelling to the capitals of the warring feudal princes offering their services as agents and emissaries. All this time Confucius was in search of a ruler or heir apparent who would allow himself to be moulded by him into the model ruler. His search was apparently unsuccessful. At about the age of sixty-eight he returned to his native state and resumed his studies. He lived only four or five more years, during which time he set about compiling commentaries on the ancient books of poetry, magic and history. Together with his detailed commentaries, these works eventually became the official classics of China. He was buried with great honours near his home in the city of Ch'u-fou, where his funerary temple and surrounding precincts have been preserved right up to the present day.

The time of his main activity was the end of the sixth century and the first two decades or so of the fifth century BC, during which he rose to prominence as a trainer of *chun-tzu* (gentlemen's sons). Confucius described himself as a transmitter rather than an originator, insisting that his purpose was not so much to impart knowledge as to inculcate moral principles, develop character, and pass on in an unaltered form a great tradition of the past.

This 'great tradition' is set out in his short classic, *The Great Learning*, in which are outlined the principal methods of Confucian instruction. To begin with, students were instructed at a very fundamental level. This was the preparatory stage (scale) of development, at which the student was sworn to uphold the so-called Three Universal Virtues: Humanity, Wisdom and Courage. From such a 'sound' psychological base it was then considered possible for the developing individual to proceed up into the next, potentially transcendental stage (scale) of self-realization, delineated by Confucius himself as the eight successive Steps of Learning. So:

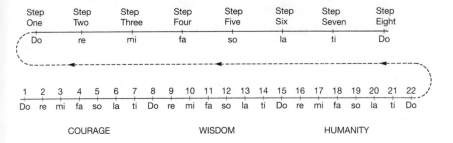

As we can see, the system of self-realization taught by Confucius was in essence identical to those of his Near and Middle Eastern counterparts, and was designed simply in order to assist the student in his efforts to transcend the ordinary bounds of space and time by 'living out' a full, sincere and therefore harmonious octave of earthly existence. Confucius evidently believed, in keeping with all true 'musicians', that the completed optimum development of a living octave in space and time opens up immense and unimaginable possibilities for the individual concerned. We have already examined the theory at the root of this belief. If any given 'humanized' octave is indeed harmonious and so able to become proportionately blended with the omnipotent forces of nature, then it can interpenetrate, on the one hand, into the *macrocosmic* time-scale of the triple-octave of forces inherent within the greater solar and planetary sphere above and, on the other, into the *microcosmic* time-scale of the four fundamental base-notes echoed by the many billions of individual cells comprising the physical composition of the organism. Remember, 'As above . . .' Remember also that the principles of Confucian law have been the guiding light of the conscience of China for more than twenty centuries, a span of time which by all known standards can very definitely be considered as being of a macrocosmic order.

The Eight Steps of Learning represented definite stages in the harmonious development of the individual. Confucius repeatedly emphasized that the system itself, which became known as 'the Way of the One Thread', could only be approached by people who were sincere with themselves. Sincerity was the one indispensable impulse which would enable students to develop to full potential their own natures and so ultimately to partake in the real work of the transmission, across centuries and millennia, of the knowledge of the Way.

Confucianism is permeated with the idea of harmony. The Way of the One Thread – the Way of 'Jen' – was the way of humanity, of love, in which the individual led the life of a 'superior man', a gentleman of perfect virtue who, through his knowledge of hermetic lore, learned to radiate harmonious psychological influences, out first to his immediate family, and then further into the greater society in which he lived and breathed and had his being.

Confucius is believed to have spent some thirteen years in his wanderings across the states in search of worthy disciples. When he finally returned home at the behest of the dictator Chi K'ang-tzu, he instructed his followers to compile a collection of maxims drawn from then extant works on ritual. Some of the passages are believed to have filtered into the book from outside sources, but for the most part the treatise itself, known as *Lun Yu*, or the *Analects of Confucius*, is generally considered to be an accurate representation of the Master's beliefs. Here are some excerpts:

Master Yu said, 'In the usages of ritual it is harmony that is prized; the Way of the Former Kings from this got its beauty. Both small matters and great depend upon it. If things go amiss, he who knows the harmony will be able to attune them. But if harmony itself is not modulated by ritual, things will still go amiss.'

Book I, no. 12

The Master said, 'A man who is not Good, what can he have to do with ritual? A man who is not Good, what can he have to do with music?'

Book III, no. 3

When talking to the Grand Master of Lu about music, the Master said, 'Their music in so far as one can find out about it began with a strict unison. Soon the musicians were given more liberty; but the tone remained harmonious, brilliant, consistent, right on till the close.'

Book III, no. 23

The Master spoke of the Succession Dance as being perfect beauty and at the same time perfect goodness . . .

Book III, no. 25

The Succession Dance was in those days performed to the accompaniment of music believed to have been composed by the Divine Sage Shun, last of the Five August Emperors. It is said that when Confucius first heard it he did not notice what he was eating for three months afterwards.

Tzu-lu asked what was meant by the 'perfect man'. The Master said, 'If anyone had the wisdom of Tsang Wu Chung, the uncovetousness of Meng Kung Ch'o, the valour of Chuang Tzu of P'ien and the dexterity of Jan Ch'iu, and had graced these virtues by the cultivation of ritual and music, then indeed I think we might call him a 'perfect man.'

Book XIV, no. 13

Here we see a direct reference to the Three Universal Virtues, the very basis of Confucian self-development. It is interesting to note, however, that the three Virtues are here complemented by a fourth, the dexterity of Jan Ch'iu – a talent which presumably enabled the 'perfect man' to compound the first three virtues into a harmonious whole.

The Master said, 'The Makers were seven . . .'

Book XIV, no. 40

He would. The Makers were the originators of fire, agriculture, metallury, carriages, boats, the potter's wheel, the loom.

The Chief Musician Chih betook himself to Ch'i;
Kan, the leader of the band at the second course, betook himself to Ch'u;
Liao, the leader of the band at the third course went to Ts'ai;
and Ch'ueh, leader of the band at the fourth course, went to Ch'in.
The big drummer Fang Shu went within the river,
The kettle-drummer Wu went within the river Han, the minor Musican Yang and Hsiang, the player of the stone-chimes, went within the sea.'

Book XVIII, no. 9

This somewhat whimsical verse describes in clear musical terms the migration which took place when Duke Chao of Lu fled to the state of Ch'i in 517 BC. Beginning with the 'Chief Musician' and ending, after a series of seven transitions, with 'the player of the stone-chimes', the text itself is a clear and accurate description of a descending or *in*volutionary scale of resonance.

Chou had its Eight Knights:
  Elder-brother Ta
  Elder-brother Kua,
  Middle-brother T'u
  Middle-brother Hu,
  Younger-brother Yeh
  Younger-brother Hsia,
  Youngest-brother Sui
  Youngest-brother Kua.

                                            Book XVIII, no. 11

Interestingly enough, a sign that a country had reached the maximum of plenty and fertility (or 'optimum resonance') was that one woman should bear *four* pairs of twins. Of course this particular idea is by no means unique to the post-Classical Chinese school of thought. Confucius himself insisted always that he was merely a transmitter of a doctrine of the distant past; and he meant exactly what he said. His collection of maxims was drawn up by his pupils in the early centuries before Christ but, as I pointed out in an earlier chapter, more than two thousand years earlier, the Old Kingdom Heliopolitan priests of Egypt were depicting their principal god, the perfected Atum, as having given birth to *four* 'divine couples'.

All of the passages just quoted clearly show that Confucius, like the ancient Greeks, considered music to be vital as an instrument of education. In his opinion the culture *par excellence* was that established by the founders of the Chou dynasty, circa 1100 BC. To gather up the fragments of this culture and to pass them on intact was the sacred mission he said had been entrusted to him by heaven. His state of origin was regarded as the principal depository of the culture originated by King Wen, although there is a story of a visit he made to the state of Ch'i where he was witness to a musical performance superior to any he had known in his native Lu. Presumably he was at that time initiated by others into the traditional hermetic mysteries, because it was after his return that he established what he believed to be the correct ritual use of the ancestral hymns of old.

In post-Classical China there already existed a corpus of literature whose authorship lay in the remotest antiquity. Possibly the most famous of these works, to which Confucius himself was a latter-day contributor, is known today as the *I Ching*, the Chinese *Book of Changes*. The great twentieth-century pioneer of consciousness Carl Jung once said that if he had his time over again he would begin with this esoteric work. Confucius is reported to have said on one occasion, 'Give me a few more years so that I may have spent a whole fifty in study, and I believe that after all I should be fairly free from errors.'

Allegedly written by the previously mentioned King Wen, founder of the Chou dynasty and embellished by his son Tan, the Duke of Chou, some thirty or forty years later, the *Book of Changes* is venerated in China as the *pièce de résistance* of all written works. Exponents of the system are unanimous in their conviction that the whole phenomenon is in some inexplicable way alive, even consciously responsive toward the genuine aspirations of the investigator. It is regarded as all at once an oracle, a book of divination and a complete system of self-realization, containing within its passages symbolic messages relating to the correct mode of conduct of the 'superior man'.

Carl Jung says in his preface to the Wilhelm translation of the work, '(The *I Ching*) is not for the frivolous-minded and immature; nor is it for intellectualists and rationalists. It is appropriate only for thoughtful and reflective people who like to think about what they do and what happens to them.'

Used properly then, the system of the *I Ching* is a way of life, the true value of which can only be assessed through direct experience. Nevertheless, from a brief 'musical' analysis of its basic form and structure, we can at least begin to understand why great thinkers like Confucius and Jung, and indeed countless millions of otherwise quite ordinary people, should have been so profoundly affected by the *I Ching*.

The whole system is constructed from eight fundamental trigrams. These eight linear symbols are each taken to represent certain attributes which blend and change one with another to produce from their combinations a total of *sixty-four* hexagrams. (Sixty-four, remember, was the number of Brahmins called upon by the Buddha's father to interpret his wife's dream.) Each hexagram is composed of *two trigrams* and is accompanied by a passage which has been designed to induce a contemplative response in the reader, so assisting in the development of the latent powers of intuition believed hidden within the unconscious.

An appendix to the *I Ching* gives an account of the origin of the eight trigrams:

In the system of the Yi [*I Ching*] there is the Great Extreme, which produced the two I (Elementary Forms). These two Forms produced the four Hsiang (Emblematic Symbols); which again produced the eight Kwa (or trigrams). The eight Kwa served to determine the good and evil (issues of events), and from this determination there ensued the (prosecution of the) great business of life.

App. III, 1, 2, 70–71

The Great Extreme and the two I – probably the origin of the Tao–Yin–Yang formula of Zen Buddhism – taken together represent the trinity itself, the universal law of three. The four Emblematic Symbols, from which the eight trigrams were derived, form the 'sound' base upon which the whole rests, the four base-notes.

All of these symbols can be described with diagrammatic certainty. A whole line (——) and a divided line (– –) are the two I. These two symbols, the positive and negative attributes of the universal process, correspond with the Brahma and Siva of Hindu mythology, and with Ormazd and Ahriman of Zoroastrian origin (i.e. the Great Extreme, the Hindu god Vishnu and the Zoroastrian god of time, Zurvan, are all one).

The two lines of the I placed over themselves and each of them over the other form the four Hsiang:

$$\equiv\ \ \underline{\ }\underline{\ }\ \ \overline{\ \ }\underline{\ }\ \ =\ =$$

These same two lines placed successively over the four Hsiang form the eight fundamental Kwa:

$$\equiv\equiv\quad \underline{\ }\underline{\ }\quad \overline{=}\underline{\ }\quad \underline{=}\underline{\ }\quad \overline{=}\overline{=}\quad \underline{=}\underline{=}\quad \overline{=}=\quad =\ =$$

The addition to each of these trigrams of each of the two I lines produces sixteen figures of four lines; in the same fashion these four lines produce thirty-two figures of five lines; and a similar operation with these produces the sixty-four hexagrams.

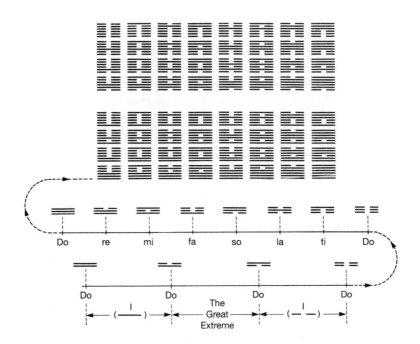

Music in action. The *Book of Changes* is hermetically composed throughout. Not only does its basic structure describe exactly the evolutionary processes of creation, its unique system of consultation also simultaneously enables the questioner to partake of the same cosmic rhythm.

Now let us look at the relationship which exists between book and practitioner. In practice one is supposed to fix a certain question in mind and then divide at random a clutch of yarrow stalks (or, as is done frequently these days, toss three coins) three times to obtain the linear signals of the upper trigram and three times to obtain the signals of the lower. The two together combine to designate one of the sixty-four hexagrams and its concomitant text, each describing an archetypal condition in human life and considered applicable to the student in respect of the question posed. Traditionally the book is consulted using the yarrow method. Fifty stalks make up the whole, but one is put aside at the outset and plays no further part. The remaining forty-nine are then divided, as we have said, at random (that is, through the free element of 'chance' and in a fundamentally impartial manner) – and subsequently counted. The stalks are actually divided three times to determine each line of a given hexagram, which means that the whole process involves a total of *six* threefold movements.

After this the practitioner progresses on to the *seventh* stage in the process – the contemplation of the text itself. He or she has reached a clearly defined 'sabbath' in an octave of personal time. Presumably King Wen's intention when devising this particular system of consultation was to put the student through an essentially musical and therefore psychologically harmonious routine. Each time a hexagram is called up, one of the hermetic texts comes to the fore and the seventh, passive or 'receptive' stage of creation is duly remembered. Not only that, the passages are deeply philosophical. In order to grasp their true meaning intuition has to be given free rein, logic left behind. The whole system is a perfect vehicle through which the mind can transcend the constricting parameters of dualistic perception; it is pure psychological music.

The raw material of music is, as we know, 'resonance', of which there is an infinite number of varying degrees which endlessly transmute one into another, deflect one another and so on. Part one of the *Ta Chuan*, or the *Great Treatise*, an appendix to the *I Ching*, describes this same process in the following way:

> Heaven is high, the earth is low; thus the Creative and Receptive are determined. In correspondence with this difference between low and high inferior and superior places are established. Movement and rest have their definite laws; according to these, firm and yielding lines are differentiated.
>
> App. III, 1, 1, 1

This seems clear enough. The eight Kwa, or notes, composed of unbroken lines (positive attributes) and broken lines (negative), were conceived of as images of all that happens in heaven and earth. At the same time they were held to be in a state of *transition*, continually changing one into another. Attention therefore centres not on things in their condition of being, but upon their movements in change, upon their ever-shifting degrees of 'resonance' up and down the particular scale to which they owe their temporal or spatial allegiance.

The very title of the book itself, then, is no arbitrary appendage. The work is exactly what it is claimed to be: it is a book of *change*, of transition, intended, through the neutral medium of the forty-nine yarrow stalks, to inculcate a taste for harmonious, intuitive action and development within the psyche of the aspirant.

There is one final point of interest concerning the basic form and structure of the *I Ching*, and this lies in the number of hexagrams which constitute the whole. According to James Legge in his translation of the work, no (Chinese) writer has yet tried to explain why the framers stopped with sixty-four hexagrams, instead of going on to 128 figures of seven lines, 256 of eight, 512 of nine, and so on indefinitely. It is an interesting question, one which has puzzled scholars for millennia; but when approached from a simple musical perspective, the reason for adopting a format of sixty-four becomes immediately apparent.

The hermetic formula, 'As above, so below' is expressed by the *upper* and *lower* trigrams of each hexagram, of which there are sixty-four possible combinations. Sixty-four, as we know, is the square of eight; and the number eight – the number of fundamental trigrams – is *the* constant, representing one complete and harmonious octave.

We have already established the fact that all possibilities can be realized by any given phenomenon when it has evolved up to a condition of optimum resonance. In other words, all possibilities are realizable within a complete and harmonious octave of resonance, because, quite simply, it *is* harmonious and so can blend in with the next scale of resonance above and with the next scale below. It should, therefore, be able to square itself; and the *I Ching*, with its sixty-four haunting and prosaic portents, represents just such a phenomenon in literary form. So, in representing the measure of what is, in effect, a quantum leap from the microcosmic scale into the macrocosmic, eight to sixty-four in fact corresponds to a ratio of zero to infinity – a detail which leads one to the inevitable conclusion that the compilers of the sixty-four hexagrams actually stopped where they did simply because there was no need to continue. The key to infinity had already been found: it was the *square of the constant*, eight. In fact, the popular game of chess is a perfect example of the unique, transcendental properties of an octave squared. Played on a board comprising sixty-four squares, it encompasses, relatively speaking, an *infinite* number of strategic possibilities.

CHAPTER EIGHT

Pure psychological music

> Unregulated, disorderly, unrhythmical, tuneless move-
> ment, and all else that partakes of evil is destitute of all
> number, and of this a man who means to die happy must be
> convinced.
>
> Plato, *Epinomis*, 978A

Circa 570 BC. This approximate point in time saw marked changes
in the evolutionary development of human consciousness. Buddhism and Zoroastrianism arose in the Near and Middle East;
Confucianism and Taoism took root in the Far East and China.
Clearly a remarkable era by any standard, it was an age which, in
the West, was to produce its own particular shade, its own unique
tone of hermetic philosophy.

About a year before the Sakya Queen Maya gave birth to her
'immaculate' child in the foothills of Nepal, Pythagoras was born
on the Greek island of Samos. Hailed by the modern writer Colin
Wilson as the first great initiate, Pythagoras, like Zoroaster, the
Buddha and Confucius, was in fact a follower himself. He was an
initiate, certainly, but with the Great Pyramid as a temporal pointer
– a structural embodiment of the formula *pi* which even then was
over two thousand years old – it can reasonably be assumed that
Pythagoras was by no means the first.

Better known in the West for his researches into geometry and
mathematics, it was Pythagoras who first coined the word
'philosopher', which means 'lover of wisdom'. Actually he was

interested in everything, all aspects of knowledge; and this showed through in him even as a youth. Recognizing his son's natural aptitude for learning, Pythagoras' father, at that time a wealthy merchant, brought his influence to bear on the dictator of Samos to send him with an introduction to the Pharaoh Amasis of Egypt. Also schooled in Babylon (instructed, some have said, by Zoroaster himself), Pythagoras retranslated the sacred canon of the trinity of octaves and transmitted it, through the musical and mathematical disciplines still being practised to this day, into the psychological presence of millions. It is true that later Greek scholars also made their indelible marks in history but, in the centuries before Christ, the musically based system of education developed by the Pythagorean school was virtually without peer.

Before looking at the more significant features of Greek revelation, however, it might be useful to outline in brief the general history of practical music, the origins of which can be traced back to a time before the pyramid era. In most if not all of the early civilizations, music ultimately developed as a complementary aspect of the hermetic phenomenon, but on every continent of the Old World it seems to have begun as a secular art, only later finding full expression at spiritual gatherings. As one might expect, all the earlier scales were experimental, incomplete, and bore little resemblance to the later Greek, seven-tone or heptatonic scale – the parent of the diatonic scale of modern times.

In Egypt itself, practical music is believed to have originated when farmers took to striking sticks together to frighten away birds. Eventually the sticks came to be used rhythmically, usually as an accompaniment to working songs and to ritual dances intended to invoke a plentiful harvest. It has been suggested, incidentally, though never actually verified, that the massive stones of the pyramids were also hauled into position by teams of men chanting in rhythm. Music in Egypt very soon became an integral part of ordinary cultural existence. In the Cairo Museum there is a set of clay figures believed to have been buried in a tomb almost five thousand years ago which depict Egyptian gentry being serenaded by three singers clapping in rhythm to the accompaniment of a harpist. The Egyptians regarded the human voice as the most effective of all instruments and priests were rigorously trained in singing, usually to the strains of the harp or the aulos (a primitive form of bagpipe), the trumpet or the sistrum (a metal rattle).

Possibly the simplest method of obtaining a series of different but compatible notes is that of dividing vibrating strings into halves, thirds, quarters and fifths. This produces a sequence of notes known today as the harmonic series of the major chord. The harmonic series has in fact been known from the earliest times. As far back as 3000 BC it was used not only in Egypt, but in Sumeria also and even as far away as China. In practice, the Egyptians used what was later to become known as the Greek pentatonic scale of Olympus, an incomplete octave of five notes based on a melodic interval of the harmonic series known as a 'perfect fourth', or the 'tetrachord'. Variations of the pentatonic scale were used contemporaneously in China (based on a series of 'perfect fifths'), and subsequently in India and in Greece. Even today it is used in the folk music of Ireland, Scotland and Bengal.

Possibly as early as the third millennium BC, the Sumerians, who settled in the region of modern Iraq, were using a reed wind instrument and a drum in the ritual worship of their various nature gods. By about 2400 BC they had flutes, tambourines, rattles and several plucked string instruments. Similar instruments were used by the Babylonians, whose first dynasty of kings was founded in 2105 BC. As with the Sumerian and early Egyptian, Babylonian music began as a secular art and was only later adapted for use at temple services. This is probably why the first known scales were incomplete. Not until the early years of the first millennium BC did the complete octave find its way into the science of harmonics. Adjacent to Babylon was warlike Assyria, situated on the banks of the River Tigris. The Assyrians effectively widened the scope of 'popular' music by using it to very real effect at banquets and military occasions. Their troupes of dancers and travelling minstrels were always received with great enthusiasm at the Egyptian courts.

As we saw in earlier chapters, in China and in Vedic India music was regarded as one of the finer arts. Documents believed to date back to around 3000 BC show that the Chinese had found that a series of 'perfect fifths' (a fifth is an 'overtone' and is produced by touching a vibrating string lightly at one-fifth its length) will produce twelve separate notes before the notes begin repeating. Set down in pitch series, these twelve notes include all the semitones of our westernized octave, which consists, as we know, of seven fundamental notes per scale. The thirteenth note, seven octaves higher, is the same as the first.

So highly did the Chinese regard the discovery of this 'circle of fifths', they held that the number five itself was a sacred unit. They also attached great importance to the ever-present symbol of the octave – the number of basic trigrams in the *I Ching* – although in practice they developed the 'circle of fifths' into a five-tone, ascending pentatonic scale. Later, influenced perhaps by the hermetic order which flourished at the time of the great Chou culture, they extended the series by two more intervals to produce the fundamental notes needed to complete a major Western scale.

But in fact, as the Chinese knew by observation, the 'circle of fifths' was slightly imperfect. That is, provided the fifths are all perfectly tuned, say on a violin, when you come back to the note with which you started, it will have gone perceptibly sharp. This means, of course, that practical music based on the harmonic series can never be fully harmonious; i.e. the notes played can never resonate at *absolute* optimum frequencies, because this natural discrepancy is always there. Pythagoras eventually established the precise mathematics of this difference and it subsequently became known as the 'Pythagorean comma'. As we shall see, the comma is crucial to a proper understanding of the ancient science of transcendental evolution, which, unlike ordinary practical musical notation, is concerned primarily with notes which *are* absolutely harmonious with all the forces of nature.

Like Pythagoras, Confucius taught that music reflected the natural harmony existing between heaven and earth. In Chinese tradition the number three corresponded to heaven and two corresponded to the earth, so notes whose frequencies of vibrations were in the ratio 3:2 were thought to have a special affinity with one another. This ratio exists, for example, between the notes 'Do' (C) and 'so' (G), which means that the former note, 'Do', vibrates two-thirds as fast as 'so' above it. The pitch interval between such notes is called a 'perfect fifth'. Starting on the note 'fa' (F) and then proceeding upwards by intervals of a 'perfect fifth' gives 'fa' (F), 'Do' (C), 'so' (G), 're' (D) and 'la' (A) – notes which, when arranged within the range of one octave, give the pentatonic scale already mentioned.

Music in India, which appeared much later than in China, was introduced around 1500 BC by Aryan migrants. Like the Egyptians, the Indians regarded the human voice as the most powerful vehicle of musical and spiritual expression. They too had instruments, mainly stringed, flutes and reed wind, but these were used predominantly at more secular gatherings, such as those providing entertainment, dancing and so on. Again, as in China, Vedic priests believed that their various vocal chants were composed by divine ancestors (Manu for example) and they ascribed different melodic forms to such regular (or rhythmic) events as the time of day, the days of the week, the passing of each of the four seasons and so on. As I mentioned in a previous chapter, even the *Vedas*, the first of the four main bodies of Vedic religious texts, were chanted in temples according to a rigidly set out musical system of exposition, which employed three priests singing in three different pitches of voice and in three different rhythms. As we know, centuries later Guatama the Buddha set out to reform the timeworn Vedic religion; and it is perhaps no coincidence that he too should have been well-versed in the art of practical music, often expounding his doctrine by reference to the established principles of audible harmony. A form of pentatonic scale was also used in Vedic India, but it is known that in the time of the Buddha the format of seven notes – especially in musical performances on religious occasions – was in common usage. The seven notes and their relative values are named in some of the earliest Vedic texts. The notes were further subdivided into subsidiary units called *shrutis*, a Sanskrit word meaning 'sympathetic note', of which, significantly, there were originally twenty-two.

In the Jewish tradition also, music in the form of rhythmic chanting has always been regarded as one of the foremost spiritual activities. Such are the Psalms, for example, or the Song of Solomon, or the emotive refrain of the cantor still heard in synagogues today. The practice probably started with Moses, who expressed the essence of all musical theory through his creation of the twenty-two-cupped menorah, the sacred octave of light used in ritual through the ages by untold millions of Jews. According to Clement of Alexandria, Moses was a practising musician who received his training from Egyptian priests. In *Numbers* 29.1, we read how he introduced an annual musical event heralded as 'a day of blowing the trumpets unto you'. There were two kinds of trumpet: the shofar, the traditional one made from a ram's horn as used by the great warrior-musician Joshua, and a silver one called the hozozra, the kind Moses is instructed to make in *Numbers* 10.2.

David, the great Jewish Psalm-writer, was also an accomplished musician, reputedly able to play the lyre like no other. During his reign (1010–975 BC) he set out the music to be used in the ritual of the Temple and was personally involved in appointing Temple musicians. It is hardly surprising that the builder of the Temple, his son Solomon, should also have attached great importance to the principles of music. On completion of the Temple complex, which measured in years took a fundamental octave of time to build, he engaged 120 priests to inform the people by sounding out their trumpets, lyres and harps. The celebrated Levite singers were also present at the dedication; they provided the essential spiritual ingredient of the all-powerful human voice.

By the time of the reign of Nebuchadnezzar II (circa 605–562 BC), Babylon had become the cultural centre of Chaldea, a highly sophisticated civilization whose court astrologers, magicians and mathematicians were the leading scholars of their day. It was here that the theoretical music of the West first began to take shape. Like most of their predecessors, the Chaldeans found that by dividing a vibrating string into halves, thirds, quarters and fifths, they could obtain a series of harmonically compatible notes. This series of notes, as I said earlier, subsequently became known as the harmonic series, the primary components of the major chord.

The Chaldean musical scale is believed to have had seven notes. As was the case with their Buddhist, Zoroastrian and Greek contemporaries, they regarded the number seven as being the most fundamental unit in nature. Their astrologers adopted the system of observation first used by the Egyptians – that of dividing the night sky into seven distinct sectors – and their ancient division of time was no less musical, with one month comprising *four* basic weeks of *seven* days apiece. It was in Chaldea that attempts were first made to approach practical music directly by means of numbers and exact proportions, but the Chaldean magi were probably greatly influenced by both Zoroastrian and Jewish streams of thought, so it is impossible to give any one school sole credit for having introduced mathematics into the problems of audible harmony. In any case it was Pythagoras who ultimately gave a real scientific basis for Western musical theory. As is known, Pythagoras studied both in Egypt and Babylon. When he finally returned to Samos he conducted scientific experiments which established proper, verifiable connections between music and mathematics.

Of all ancient civilizations, there has been none which has held music in as high regard as classical Greece, where it dominated almost every aspect of life. Greek philosophers and metaphysicians proclaimed a divine origin for music, referring to the 'harmony of the spheres', a perfect cosmic balance of forces whence human harmony must ultimately stem. In Greek mythology, Apollo, son of Zeus, was both a warrior and a master musican and was said to have dwelt on Mount Parnassus with the celebrated nine female Muses (making a decad of divines). The Muses – from where came the word 'music' itself – were the sources of inspiration of all the arts, including history, sacred lyrics, dancing and astronomy.

The early Greeks regarded music as the great 'civilizing' factor. They believed in the doctrine of the *ethos*, the effects of the different *nomes* (styles) of music on men. In Plato's opinion music and athletics were the two main elements of a proper education; Aristotle, too, believed that the right kind of musical training played an invaluable role in the shaping of an individual's character.

But in fact, as we have seen from earlier discussion, this fundamentally musical vision of universal reality describes a pattern of evolutionary development which has actually been the blueprint from which all major, pre-Christian religious doctrines have been drawn. Our journey across time must continue, of course, because the Greeks, as we shall see, were by no means the last great nation to nurture genuine, 'thrice-great' initiates. As the reader might by now have come to realize, the revelationist is a member of an exclusive, undying race of musically orientated giants who have time and again proved themselves capable of generating influences, or forms of 'intelligent resonance', which have the power to permeate through the darker world of the ordinary human psyche as easily and naturally as physical sunlight penetrates constantly out into the eternal blackness of space.

So to the ancients in general, and in particular the Greeks, musical form and notation was universally regarded as the principal vehicle of wisdom. It represented a divine embodiment of a hidden code, a sacred canon whose inner composition held the conceptual key to man's spiritual liberation. In applying the fundamental tenets of the code to every aspect of their lives, the esoteric orders of virtually every great civilization of the past were effectively utilizing the single, most efficient means of projecting their highly developed refining influences across vast expanses of space and time. Consequently, even to this day, in the fast-moving, consumer-oriented twentieth century, the original hermetic ideas of these metaphysicians of ancient times are still being studied and followed by students of philosophy and ethics the world over.

The Classical Greek movement itself received its greatest impetus from the early Pythagorean schools. Their principal aim, like that of their Egyptian forerunners, was simply to 'echo the music of the spheres', to 'tune in' to the harmonious forces constantly at play in the world of nature. Just as the Old Kingdom vizier Shemaj and his unnamed son had done, the Pythagorean mystics organized the whole of their lives to conform with the natural, rhythmic flow of events. Moreover they ultimately either developed or rediscovered (probably the latter) a unique, practical method of using the hidden power of 'esoteric music' to its fullest possible advantage. Before this can be properly explained, however, it will be necessary to examine in some detail the basic principles of Greek musical theory itself, within which is to be found the key to many a locked door – not the least of them being the one behind which lies the definitive answer to the ever-recurring question of the decad.

The basis of most of the practical music of Classical Greece was the standard unit known as the 'tetrachord', a melodic interval of four notes called a 'perfect fourth' – for example, 'so' (G) up to 'Do' (C), or 'la' (A) up to 're' (D). Being part of the harmonic series, the two extreme notes were regarded as fixed, although two more notes could be inserted between the outer ones, so that a 'so–Do' tetrachord might consist of four notes: 'so–la–ti–Do' (G A B C). By then connecting one tetrachord onto another, with two of the notes overlapping and including one extra note at the bottom, the Greeks developed a heptatonic scale known as the 'greater perfect system'. Being sevenfold in structure, it bore some resemblance to the seven-tone scales of Chaldea and India.

We know there are eight fundamental notes in a given, standard major scale, and that all of the vibrations of the first seven are contained within the eighth transcendental note. In being composed of all the degrees of resonance comprising the notes below, this transcendental note has the power to exceed the scale of its origin and become, simultaneously, a single new note again, but on a higher plane of existence, i.e. in the next scale above.

As I said earlier, the Pythagoreans were the first investigators to record the exact vibratory ratios which ultimately established the distinct series of notes upon which most of our modern Western music is based. They verified mathematically that an ascending octave represented the measure of the *doubling* of the rate of vibrations within any given major scale (i.e. the first note 'Do' vibrates half as fast as the eighth note 'Do').

They also realized, however, that the change in the frequency of pitch between each individual note is not the same throughout. Between the third and fourth notes, 'mi–fa' (E–F) and the seventh and eighth notes, 'ti–Do' (B–C), the interval contains only a half-pitch or half-tone, whereas the intervals between the other notes consist of whole tones. (A 'tone' refers to the frequency of vibrations of any given sound; a 'note' refers to the relative length in time the sound lasts.) In other words, at certain points in the development of a natural octave the vibrations will accelerate uniformly; at others, their rate of increase naturally retards, thus causing a certain amount of evolutionary deviation.

The major scale was thus formed by moving upwards from the base-note using the following intervals: tone, tone, semitone, tone, tone, tone, semitone. Obviously the semitone intervals mark the points where the rate of increase of vibrations naturally retards. So:

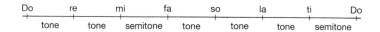

Do	re	mi	fa	so	la	ti	Do
tone	tone	semitone	tone	tone	tone	semitone	

This formula subsequently gave rise to the first 'chromatic' scale, which consisted of twelve notes. 'Chromatic' comes from the Greek root word meaning the use of 'colour' (chromos) in the same way as one speaks of 'shades of emotion'. The chromatic scale was derived simply by dividing the whole tones into half-tones, thus introducing five additional semitones between the fundamental notes of the heptatonic scale, so that the natural major scale could be divided into twelve individual parts, thus:

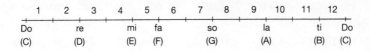

In practice, the chromatic and heptatonic scales were rarely employed by the Greeks. They represented theoretical concepts, to be used primarily as philosophical aids to the study of the natural mechanics of the universe. Whilst both scales manifested an audible harmony, pleasing to the ear, they still fell perceptibly short of the real thing. Just as the Chinese had realized when they devised their 'circle of fifths', the Pythagoreans discovered that the audible harmony of natural music was marginally imperfect. Something in nature was slightly amiss – hence the inclusion of the Pythagorean comma in the equation of the twelve tones of the chromatic scale.

In the observable world, of course, this kind of harmonic deviation is natural. From the widest horizon down to the most minute serrations on a single leaf, nature's physical realm is littered with 'curves', 'angles', 'waves' and so on. Similarly the world of human nature – which *is* 'music', remember – is a world of ceaseless deviation. This is why a man who sets out to do one thing can very often end up doing quite the opposite, or nothing at all, and why objective concepts such as those realized by individuals like, say, Einstein or Jesus Christ can subsequently develop into totally unexpected, 'cacophonous' phenomena like the holocausts of Hiroshima and Nagasaki, or the dreadful Inquisition. In actual fact, all of us deviate or lose control at some time or another, perhaps by breaking a promise or a confidence, either to ourselves or our friends or our peers. This is inevitable for in the natural world, which is home for most of us, there are no 'straight lines' to be found. Everything moves, everything turns, twists, fights for more room in space and time. At present man likes to think of himself as the undisputed lord of mammals, the 'crown of creation' as it were

– which is really something of a misnomer for a creature who lives so much of his life being almost totally unaware of his real self and of his proper place in the cosmic scheme of things. Obviously the 'crown of creation' should not fantasize, should not kill or make war, should not sit back in a dreamlike state of complacency, idly coveting some unwitting neighbour's ox as millions starve; and yet he does these things unceasingly, often without even manifesting a single spark of self-awareness.

So nothing ordinary man does is constant in a conscious way. Nothing can be said to be harmonious in the fullest sense. And this includes, as I said before, the seven-tone musical scale itself, of which the Pythagorean comma is an integral part. The uneven periods of development between the fundamental notes of a major scale thus give us an exact picture, in musical terms, of the mode of progression through space and time of all *natural* phenomena, great or small, material or otherwise.

Of course, *supernatural* phenomena occur continuously, but in general we tend to overlook them, either because they are so commonplace as to appear natural, or because they occur on a macrocosmic scale and so cannot be formulated in terms of three-dimensional logic. Consider the miracle of the creation of a new life, for example, or the extreme psychological potency of religion and the scriptures, or even the unique power of music itself, which in one form or another is able to strike a chord in everyman. Pythagoras, who gained a reputation as something of a 'miracle-worker' himself, actually had a special symbol with which he identified the paranormal. This was the sacred tetrad (the *tetraktys*), which was usually expressed by placing ten pebbles on the ground like this:

One of the most important symbols in Pythagorean mysticism, and which Pythagoras in his *Golden Verses* defined as the 'source of Nature' and 'models of the gods', the tetrad was identified with the harmonious 'song of the Sirens', later described by Plato as the 'music of the spheres'. 'Gods', 'Sirens' and 'spheres' all refer to the sun and its visible planets, each of which was represented by one of the deities of the Greek pantheon. As a 'model', the tetrad was considered applicable to things both 'above' and 'below', its inner composition not only reflecting the supernatural nature of the 'gods', but of perfected men also. Thus the underlying structure describes, in terms of music and octaves, the successive stages in the harmonious development of an evolving human being. The first stage, or scale, of development, denoted by the four primary or base pebbles, represents the preparatory stage of evolution – the four 'sound' base-notes upon which is constructed the whole. This corresponds to the *physical* body of man, which is the product of the process of biological integration of the three interpenetrating orders of organic matter: matter in electronic state (active), matter in molecular state (intermediary) and matter in cellular state (passive).

From the harmonious interaction of these three octaves of energy and form is born the last base-note (the fourth pebble), a phenomenon which, according to the laws of musical theory, contains all the qualities of the preceding twenty-one notes. Upon being struck, this fourth base-note simultaneously transcends the physical scale of development and so transmits a single new note up into the next scale of existence. This transcendental signal, as we know from the first law of nature, is itself composed of three interpenetrating orders of energy and form – hence the three pebbles at the second stage in the development of the tetrad. This second level corresponds to the *psychological* body of the individual, a presence born of the three nerve-complexes responsible for sensations, emotions and perceptions or impressions. Sensations (ideally) should be active, emotions intermediary, and the mind itself, in receiving impressions, in being impressed, must therefore be passive.

Obviously the four 'base' pebbles of the tetrad represent a completed, fully resonant triple-octave. Nature herself has seen to it that the body's cellular structure resonates at optimum potential. This second, psychological level, however, represents another, potentially higher, but as yet incomplete triple-octave. That is, the next, transcendental or metaphysical, fourth 'base' has yet to be realized, presumably through some kind of process of self-development. Assuming such a process exists, then these three inner octaves of psychological energy and form, having successfully evolved up to a condition of optimum resonance, would then combine together to generate a single new note up into an even higher scale of existence.

So, theoretically at least, this would be the ideal human condition: active body, neutral emotions and passive or receptive mind, perfect harmony head to toe. Of course it would be quite impractical for ordinary workaday man permanently to maintain this kind of psychological posture. Those who remained passive throughout would run the obvious risk of being trampled underfoot in the frenzied, 'natural' world of the upwardly mobile. It was for this very reason that the concept of the 'sabbath' was first introduced. The sabbath is a temporal expression of the cosmic note 'ti', the seventh, passive day in a fundamental octave of time, or the period of rest during which the qualitative aspects of the previous week's activities should be reflected upon in an impartial manner and subsequently compounded into a harmonious, receptive concentration of psychological energy and form. (Basically this is simply the passive act of meditation, or contemplation, the importance of which is emphasized in all religious doctrines. More of this later.)

Assuming the three 'octaves' at the second level of the tetrad (the three orders of energy and form: sensations, emotions and perceptions) are complete and harmonious in the earthly sense, this means that the next stage of evolution, denoted by the two pebbles at the third level, must represent an *extension of existence* up to the threshold of spheres which lie beyond those determined by our ordinary powers of perception. We cannot, therefore, speak of this stage in ordinary phenomenological terms.

At this third stage then, the individual now has the potential to exceed his own time-scale and become part of a much greater entity. Consequently the individual himself is here represented by just *one* of the two pebbles. The second pebble represents the unknown, the opposite of this greatest of unions.

This is the Same and the Other of Platonic invention. Parallel examples of this sacred union are to be found expressed in many of the earlier-discussed forms of hermetic symbolism. On the Hebraic menorah it is represented by the two sets of three which constitute the six subordinate branches; in the Talmud it is described as the unification of the 'sanctuary that is above' and the 'sanctuary that is below'. Zoroaster portrayed it as the final meeting with Good Mind through the medium of Truth; and, in the Chinese *Book of Changes*, which gives us what is perhaps the best description of all, the process is symbolized by the upper and lower trigrams of each of the sixty-four hexagrams.

The last pebble of the tetrad, standing supreme and alone at the very pinnacle of evolutionary development, represents the ultimate goal of all initiates: the transcendental, 'hermetically sealed' signal of the whole evolutionary phenomenon – *total illumination*, the point at which the Same and the Other are united as one, and where all possibilities are realized.

We now come to what is certainly the most important aspect of the tetrad, for not only does its basic structure contain within it a description of the pattern of development of an evolutionary, or 'intelligent', scale of resonance, it also gives a precise description of the means by which the desired optimum resonance of such a scale may be achieved.

Remember that, in the world of nature, there exist two kinds of octave. There are *natural*, involutionary or descending octaves, and there are *supernatural*, evolutionary or ascending octaves – those which actually reach a condition of optimum resonance and so square their possibilities.

The material world of natural octaves begins with the subatomic particle, the finest order of materiality open to scientific investigation. These innumerable and minuscule particles of matter condense, through space and time, into gross planetary form. This is the Same, the world of measurable phenomena described in geometric terms by Plato as being a single, whole circle. This physical world, as Plato understood it, is a complete and harmonious entity whose evolutionary path has already been trod, and in which all (material) possibilities have been realized. But then, as one can deduce from the pyramid-shaped structure of the tetrad, the whole process also has the possibility to work in reverse. This is the Other side of the universal coin, the process of 'transcendental evolution' (the evolution of 'life', of consciousness), which begins, in fact, where the Same has ended. So *descent*, from the subatomic particle down into gross planetary form, is the Same; *ascent*, from the basic elements of the earth into the immeasurable stuff of human consciousness, is the Other. The third, reconciliatory force, the mediator between the two coordinates, is of course musical form itself, the Platonic 'essence'.

But now, to express the secret of secrets itself we must briefly reconsider the patterns of *acceleration* and *retardation* discovered by the Greeks in their experiments with the natural development of the vibrations of sound in air. The Pythagoreans proposed that, for evolutionary or 'intelligent' octaves to have a fully harmonious 'ring' to them, it was necessary to exceed the bounds of ordinary practical music and actually introduce the two additional concentrations of resonance at the points of vibrational retardation – between the notes 'mi–fa', and 'ti–Do'. These additional concentrations of resonance, or 'metaphysical semitones', were to be created, in time, by the individual himself. Remember the seven-tone octave of practical music reflects a natural cosmic process which is in reality disharmonious. That is, without the two additional semitone 'shocks' it is not possible for a developing scale of 'intelligent' resonance to exactly *double* its rate of vibrations and so *square* its possibilities. In other words, in lacking the aforementioned semitones the natural, living octave must, given time, either 'decompose' (involve), or be deflected or consumed by other more powerful orders of energy and form passing through its given sphere of influence – hence the vast multiplicity of natural forms existing in the universe and why, as has already been suggested, there are no apparent straight lines in nature.

According to the principles at the root of the tetrad however, there *are* 'straight lines' to be found, lines which have to be developed by the participant, by the 'musician' himself. So, by introducing the two additional semitones between the stages of development delineated by the notes 'mi–fa' and 'ti–Do', these Greek adepts quite literally succeeded in achieving the impossible; they actually fought against nature and won. And in so doing they realized that the supernatural path to enlightenment was in reality diametrically opposed to the so-called 'constant' forces of nature.

This idea can best be described through our usual diagrammatic format. The natural, *involving* octave, in lacking the required semitones between the fundamental notes 'mi–fa' and 'ti–Do', would develop like so:

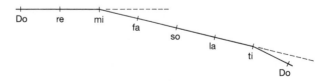

But the completed evolutionary tetrad – the *harmonious* or cosmic octave – containing within its composition the additional concentrations of resonance, the semitone 'shocks', would appear like this:

We now have a chain of nine successive intervals. And from the first law of nature we know that this octave is itself composed of three interpenetrating orders of energy and form; it has active properties, it has neutral properties and it has passive properties. It is therefore possible to subdivide this original chain of nine links into three subordinate sets of three links each; that is, into three subordinate, inner octaves of energy and form:

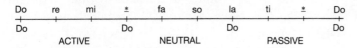

with four 'sound' bases.

This diagram represents a conventional Pythagorean expression of the consubstantial and indivisible Trinity. And the reason why there should be *ten* pebbles in the tetrad is simply that the tenth, transcendental product of the whole 'heptatonic' phenomenon is in fact the *eighth* note of the completed scale.

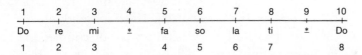

The tetrad is, I believe, the key to the whole of Revelation. Within it is to be found true harmony. It is actually the means of obtaining such a harmony, and could well be the origin of the legendary 'philosopher's stone', skilfully fashioned by none other than the original 'philosopher' himself.

The method of introducing the two missing semitones into living 'octaves' of human intelligence is relatively simple in theory, if not in practice. The second stage in the development of the tetrad provides an initial clue, the ideal human condition being linked with an active body, neutral emotions and passive mind, which means that the first semitone ('mi–fa') should be filled by active impulses and the second ('ti–Do') by some form of passive energy. (Precisely what is meant by active and passive impulses will be explained later.) Fortunately all of the world's major religious reformers taught by example and so left us with many a clue in this respect.

But in fact, this 'philosopher's stone' – if that's what it is – had existed long before Pythagoras launched it into the realms of legend and myth. For example, a clear recorded description of it is to be found in the Book of Genesis. In chapter 5 we read of the succeeding generations after Adam. Adam denotes the base-note, 'Do', of an evolving tetrad of human intelligence. 'And Adam . . . begat . . . Seth . . . and all the days that Adam lived were nine hundred and thirty years.' The text continues, in the same format, with another eight descendants – Enos, Cainan, Mahalaleel, Jared, Enoch, Methuselah, Lamech and, finally, Noah: 'And Lamech . . . begat . . . Noah . . . and all the days of Lamech were seven hundred and seventy and seven years . . .' This may be expressed as:

ADAM	Seth	Enos	Cainan	M'leel	Jared	Enoch	M'selah	Lamech	NOAH
Do	re	mi	±	fa	so	la	ti	±	Do

Significantly, at the point of the last semitone interval between the notes 'ti' and 'Do', the age of Lamech (777) is a numerical expression of the key to the Sacred Constant itself. The transcendental product of this completed evolutionary octave was, of course, the good Noah, the most famous and well-loved builder in the history of mankind. Thus Noah and his family: his wife (1), Shem (2), Shem's wife (3), Ham (4), Ham's wife (5), Japheth (6), Japheth's wife (7) – total eight, were the only people to survive, or transcend, the Flood.

But as we can see, the whole of this ancestral story of Noah, from Adam to the Deluge and beyond, is simply a hermetic description of the evolutionary development of the tetrad and of the octave. Furthermore the inner composition of the tetrad is then further described through the actions of Noah himself, who took on board his Ark *seven* pairs of all the beasts who were 'ritually clean' (the seven full notes) and *two* pairs of all the beasts who were 'unclean' (the two extra semitones).

In fact, there are numerous descriptions of a similar nature in many of the major religious doctrines of the world. The Vedic variation of this same theme is expressed in the legend of the Ten Great Sages engendered by the law-giver Manu, who between them created 'seven other Manus possessing great brilliancy . . .' Another example is the Greek myth of the god Apollo and his nine 'musical' Muses, divine patrons of all the arts. Remember also the Ten Commandments, the ten words or 'tokens' contained within the Hebraic Ark of the Covenant. Even the mysterious Kabbalah itself, the 'secret science' of Jewish mystics, describes the processes

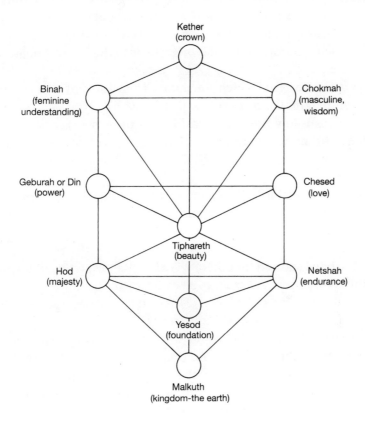

The Sephiroth: the Kabbalistic tetrad or 'tree of life'. Kether, the creative Godhead, Chokmah (masculine, active) and Binah (feminine, passive) collectively represent the trinity, the final three stages of an evolutionary octave. Man himself, who has yet to harmonize all his faculties, is a living manifestation of the seven lower Sephiroth.

of creation in terms of the ten primordial numbers and the twenty-two letters of the Hebraic alphabet. Significantly the word 'Kabbalah' means 'reception' – a process of psychic initiation calling for a fundamentally passive frame of mind.

The basis of the Kabbalah is the diagram shown, known as the 'sacred tree'. It consists of ten circles, known as the Sephiroth, which are joined together by twenty-two lines or 'paths'. The Sephiroth represent a series of nine stages through which the soul must pass to achieve union with God (Kether) and provide a graphic description of an evolutionary tetrad. The twenty-two paths show that the ten-fold 'tree', being in essence a musical phenomenon, is also composed within as a triple-octave.

The musical nature of the system is confirmed in a Kabbalistic text, which attributes the following words to the Rabbi Abbas:

> We six are lights which shine forth from a seventh; thou art the seventh light, the origin of us all.
> For assuredly there is no stability in those six, save what they derive from the seventh. For all things depend on the seventh.
> *The Great Holy Assembly*, verses 1160–1

An earlier section of the same text refers directly to both tetrad and octave and is entirely reminiscent of the law expounded by the Indian Manu:

> We have learned that there were ten (Rabbis) who entered into (the Assembly), and that seven came forth.
> *The Great Holy Assembly*, verse 1152

Theoretically no tetrad could develop uniformly without embodying the principle of the four preparatory base-notes. These are symbolized in the system by the four 'worlds' upon which the whole matrix is said to rest – three 'spiritual' and another, part visible (our physical world) and part not so.

In fact, once the principles of the tetrad have been grasped it becomes possible to understand better many other extant works of revelation. The relevant ones will be discussed in later chapters, but a further example which can be quoted here is that of the numerical formulae underlying the Hindu interpretation of world history. It may be recalled that the full cosmic cycle in Hindu mythology is known as the *kalpa*, or 'day of Brahma', lasting precisely 4,320,000,000 years. Now taken, not simply as a literal measure of time, but instead as a symbolized pattern of form and sequence, we see that the numbers themselves render an exact description of the evolutionary development of the tetrad:

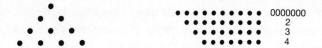

This same formula also survived in Babylon. In the library of Alexandria there once existed a three-volume history of the world, now lost, compiled by a certain Babylonian priest named Berossus. Volume one dealt with the interval from Genesis to the Flood, a period which Berossus took to be 432,000 years.

I think most of us would agree that the art of practical music has always fulfilled a particularly special role in our lives. Especially in this modern world of seemingly endless polarities, music is possibly the single, most effective medium through which untold millions of quite ordinary people can be brought together in a state of relative emotional equanimity. The 'Band-Aid' or Pavarotti concerts, televised simultaneously across continents, are prime examples of this. Performed in aid of charity, these unprecedented musical events have been seen, heard and participated in by hundreds of millions of people of every conceivable political and cultural persuasion.

The sheer expansiveness of this whole phenomenon suggests, above all, that music per se is an objective creation, an 'immaculate conception' which characteristically bears all the hallmarks of the genuine hermetic enterprise. When only thousands are involved over a time-span of mere decades, we have simply a mechanical contrivance; but when millions are involved, over centuries and millennia, we surely have the real thing. Music, then, is just that, it is the real thing; and for his ingenious contributions toward its development, Pythagoras stands unique among the great initiates of the past.

Of course the music we have come to know and love through emotional experience is just one example of the many new Greek themes. Pythagoras was a classic all-rounder, whose numerous innovations in mathematics and geometry have ultimately proved to be as resilient in the face of the unending ravages of time as the musical scale itself. Pythagoras' main role, however, was that of a teacher of the mysteries he had learned in Egypt. Like Moses, Zoroaster and the Buddha, he was primarily a revelationist; and his use of numbers, geometry and musical proportion – the whole science of which was neatly summed up in the triangular form of the tetrad – was a clear attempt to express the absolute hermetic conformity of all manifestations of nature, and in particular the individual development of the evolving human being.

It is commonly believed that the other key symbol of the hermetic sciences – the classical formula *pi* – appeared as if by accident some time in the last millennium BC. Kurt Mendelsohn, in his book *The Riddle of the Pyramids*, suggests that the Egyptians knew of the convention $\frac{22}{7}$ slightly earlier than 1000 BC but, as I mentioned in chapter two of this book, the formula was known in the days of the Old Kingdom, when the Great Pyramid was built. Moreover, not only was the formula known at that time, it was in fact practically applied to everyday human existence – as in the case of the Old Kingdom vizier and his son, who between them divided control of the twenty-two *nomes* or districts of Upper Egypt in direct accordance with the proportions described by classical *pi*; i.e. twenty-two nomes under the control of the vizier himself and seven of them under the subsidiary control of his deputy.

There is no direct record of the formula having been used in its mathematical form by Pythagoras the geometrician, but it seems fairly certain that he received initiation into its esoteric significance from Egyptian priests. Indeed, as we saw earlier, when the tetrad itself is set out in a musical format of seven fundamental notes and two extra semitones, it comprises a chain of nine intervals, three sets of three links each, with each set constituting an 'inner octave'. In this fashion the tetrad can be said to contain three inner octaves, or twenty-two subordinate notes.

The basic principles of geometry are now taught everywhere (including Pythagoras' famous theorem about the square of the hypotenuse), but in the Classical Greek era it was still a sacred art: it was regarded as the visual expression of the laws of universal harmony. Significantly the Great Pyramid itself is principally an expression in masonry of the sacred art of the geometrician. Whether or not its original function was, as is now popularly believed, to promote the union of cosmic and terrestrial forces we cannot say. When it is understood precisely what cosmic forces are and in what manner they proceed through space and time, then perhaps this particular aspect of the Pyramid's existence will become clearer. But the important point to remember is that the Pyramid is nothing if not the largest, most conspicuous symbol of absolute geometrical precision ever designed. Obviously it was when Pythagoras visited Egypt that the secret proportions of the Pyramid were revealed to him, because it was only after he returned from his travels that his highly influential hermetic career began in earnest.

In Plato's *Timaeus* there is a detailed description of the construction of two geometrical symbols known as the Same and the Other. I referred to these symbols earlier, when examining the tetrad – in particular the third stage of its development designated by the two 'pebbles'. These were diagrammatic aids employed by the author to describe the spheres beyond Euclidean, or three-dimensional, space. They represented the two opposing aspects of existence, the 'phenomenon' and the 'numinon', which, being naturally incommensurable with one another, were brought together by God through a third force – 'essence'. Both the Same and the Other were depicted as circles, but the circle of the Other was divided by drawing within it six more concentric rings. This was the Lambda, another of the 'sacred' symbols of the Pythagoreans, which was regarded as a visual expression of the underlying musical structure of the entire universe (hence the term 'cosmos', coined by Pythagoras, which means an orderly or *harmonious* whole).

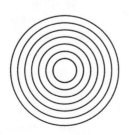

Here again Pythagoras is echoing the fundamental message of the original Egyptian doctrine, which has its identical counterparts in the concurrent cosmologies of Buddhism and Zoroastrianism. In the story of the Buddha related in an earlier chapter, we hear how, as a baby, he rose from his cushion and encompassed the whole universe in seven successive steps. These same seven spheres of existence were depicted by the Persian Magi as being ruled over by one of the seven angelic Amesha Spentas, the Bounteous Immortals of the Zoroastrian pantheon.

Although the Lambda comprises seven concentric rings, it can also be depicted otherwise, and in a way which corresponds in detail to the doctrine attributed to Moses, who, in his much misunderstood Book of Genesis, relates how God made the earth in six days and then, so to speak, put His feet up.

In this diagram, the categories of the worlds between the two Absolutes are merely generalizations, but being six in number and diminishing as they do from great to small, they can be said to correspond with the structure of the Lambda. Obviously the moon, in being the lowest or least 'resonant' order of world, is where it should be. Its parent planet, earth – a world intrinsically connected to it but at the same time one of an entirely different age and order – is also correctly placed. The true nature of worlds beyond this point can only be guessed at, but in our efforts to understand the cosmogenic implications of Pythagorean and Mosaic revelation, the categories beyond that of earth need be no more than suggestive.

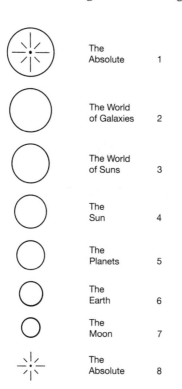

The Absolute	1
The World of Galaxies	2
The World of Suns	3
The Sun	4
The Planets	5
The Earth	6
The Moon	7
The Absolute	8

The moon, as we know, is not a planet in the full sense. It has no atmosphere of its own as yet, and is cold, still, unfinished. Note that the moon in the diagram represents the seventh note, or stage, in the creative order of worlds. The seventh stage, of course, as Moses never seemed to tire of telling his people, is the sacred Sabbath, the day of rest. Apparently God intends to make a proper planet of the moon 'tomorrow', after He has refreshed Himself.

There is an incidental clue here as to the probable origin and true meaning of the well-known Greek concept of 'geocentricity'. Modern thought has tended to regard this concept from a typically physical perspective, assuming that the Greeks naively believed the earth to be at the centre of the solar system. And yet, according to Archimedes, there was a book in the great library of Alexandria by the Greek astronomer Aristarchus of Samos which argued that the earth is one of the planets, which like them orbits the sun. Aristarchus lived about three hundred years after Pythagoras and, although he may have been the first educated Greek actually to write about the concept of 'heliocentricity', there is no particularly good reason for supposing that the idea originated with him. He did live on Samos after all, the very epicentre of early Greek esoteric activity and the place where astronomy itself ultimately became a respected Greek science. Even Copernicus himself acknowledged Pythagorean astronomical concepts as being forerunners of his hypothesis that the earth and the other planets rotate in orbit about the sun, so the early Greeks can justifiably be given the credit for having inspired a new and original train of thought.

The idea of a 'geocentric' world was possibly a corruption of the original hermetic concept of earth-centred consciousness, the evolutionary development of which *begins* on this planet (or perhaps even at a lower level, under the primary influence of lunar magnetism) and which, given the right kind of impetus, has the potential to evolve up through an ascending order of greater spheres. From a so-called 'geocentric' point of view, it would have been *life* on earth being put under subjective scrutiny, as opposed to the naive idea that the earth itself was the centre of the solar system, the sun simply a subservient ball of fire. The Greeks actually revered the sun in the form of the god Apollo. It is unlikely that those initiated into the mysteries should visualize such a mighty deity being eternally subjected to a slavish existence akin to that of a mere satellite. Aristarchus, at least, seems to have been better informed than some of the more verbose scholars of his day. Of course, if he were an initiate – and it seems likely – he would have believed, as Moses did, in the substance of Jacob's famous dream about the ladder stretching from heaven to earth, the rainbow covenant. From the earliest times, the light of the sun has always been regarded as having a superior, rather than a subservient, nature.

The Pythagoreans in particular studied everything in relation to this 'universal music' played by the sun and to the 'harmony of the spheres' and its effects on man. Their researches into number and musical proportions confirmed their belief that a proper understanding of the laws governing this cosmic order opened up a whole new world to the observer. With *pi*, remember, the archetypal symbol of absolute harmony, it was possible to square the circle. In geometrical terms the square and the circle relate one to the other as do zero and infinity – yet here was a mathematical system which, with remarkable accuracy, could bridge such a gulf. Had the formula never been revealed in the first place, later thinkers might never have realized the significance of this ratio and the most fundamental coordinates of classical geometry would have remained forever incommensurable with one another. So this was a true revelation. But of course it was not new; it was simply a natural, Western version of the original hermetic science designed to harmonize with the new psychological tempo of early Greek consciousness.

Another interesting feature of this new 'Pythagorean' life science is the concept of metempsychosis, or the 'transmigration of souls', an idea which also appeared in the form of the Buddhist and Hindu doctrine of reincarnation. Both concepts speak of what the rational mind views as the fantastic, of supernatural journeys across time and space made by the souls of men and women as they pass from one body and are born into another. Parapsychologists have long been seeking tangible evidence in favour of reincarnation, although by its very nature a nonmaterial transmigration, if it is a reality, would be an unprovable one. Some very detailed accounts of previous existences have been related during so-called periods of regression induced through hypnosis, but there is no way of telling whether they represent genuine accounts or whether they are simply fanciful by-products of an overly fertile imagination.

Some of the most elaborate case histories of claimants to previous lives come from Asia, where the possibility of projecting one's *karma* across time and space is commonly accepted as fact. Tibetan priests in particular have made of the doctrine of rebirth a virtual science. A certain time after the death of their spiritual leader, the Dalai Lama, tradition dictates that they go out in search of his new incarnation – a boy-child around two years old. When they think they have found a likely candidate, they will then put their intuition to the test by presenting the child with certain of their previous master's most personal belongings, together with other nonrelated items. It is reported that the last time they did this the young candidate, the present Dalai Lama (said to be the fourteenth successive reincarnation of the Tibetan avatar Chenrezi), showed no interest whatsoever in any item which did not belong to their former high priest. It was this response, together with the boy's satisfactory answers to some pertinent questions, which convinced the lamas of Tibet that their former leader had somehow broken through the barriers of ordinary time and space to be with them once again. Although politically exiled, he is still with them now of course, a man of obvious sincerity and great dignity and arguably one of the most respected spiritual leaders in the world today. To his followers at least, the Dalai Lama is living proof that the soul or the essence of the individual can continue to exist on another plane, or planes, after death.

In many esoteric traditions these different planes of existence have been variedly and often lucidly described. The Tibetan *Book of the Dead*, itself structured around the number seven, is actually a hitchhiker's guide to the higher planes, describing in essentially musical terms how the soul can successfully transcend on to the greater scale above, to the 'seventh bardo' and beyond. The Sephiroth of the Kabbalah are also basically a description of worlds beyond, of higher dimensions through which the soul has to pass to reach the ultimate Godhead.

This age-old belief in the existence of paranormal dimensions is as strong today as it ever was, and even though we lack the means of scientifically measuring and charting them, there are, nevertheless, many sane and rational people who believe that, in one form or another, they certainly do exist. Characteristically the logical mind, bound by convention in a three-dimensional world, has a natural tendency to visualize the spheres beyond death subjectively, almost as if they had a geographical position and were marked by coordinates in ordinary space and time. But of course, if higher dimensions do indeed exist, the geography involved in charting them might not be quite so simple.

Although it doesn't admit to the existence of a hereafter, modern science is not averse to the idea that there could be higher dimensions existing beyond ordinary time and space. In his bestselling book, *A Brief History of Time*, Stephen Hawking, the Lucasian Professor of Mathematics at Cambridge University, discusses the possibility of the existence of these other dimensions (and therefore other realities), suggesting that the reason we see only three dimensions of space and one of time is that the higher dimensions all curve up into a space of very small size, perhaps as small as a million, million, million, million, millionth of an inch. We would therefore never be able to notice such a small irregularity in ordinary space, because our minds are structured to focus only on the four conventional dimensions, a continuum which consists of only gradual curves, like the shapes and orbits of planets, or the spiral motion of galaxies. In a later chapter we shall be returning for a closer look at the modern scientific view of worlds beyond ordinary time. I have mentioned Professor Hawking's proposal here simply to show that, theoretically at least, there are other places to which the recurring 'soul' of man could temporarily migrate.

Pythagoras believed that the soul is a fallen angel, a corrupted divinity temporarily locked within the body and condemned to a cycle of rebirths within human beings or lesser life forms until such time as it is purified enough to withstand the shock of death. If we use the analogy of musical notation, as we did when examining the life of Noah, we can visualize every human soul as being a changeling, a dynamic concentration of metaphysical resonance, traversing either up or down its own particular scale according to its merits. At birth, or possibly conception, the individual's embryonic consciousness would be designated by the first note, 'Do'. Death, the top note of the scale, would also be designated by the note 'Do'. The only difference between conception and death therefore would be a difference in *scale*. The objective for all of us thus seems to be to 'become as little children', as it were, to experience 'death' (the

ultimate passive or receptive state) before it actually happens.
Presumably only then would it be possible for the soul to have a free
choice at the crucial moment of spiritual transcendence – either to
carry over fully into the greater scale above, or to return voluntarily
to the 'underworld', like the legendary Greek musician Orpheus,
and show others the way.

According to many Buddhist and Hindu commentaries, very few
individuals succeed in their lifetime in resonating in tune with the
universal overtone. Consequently the immense, supernatural
surge of power with which they are confronted at death is too much
for them; and after a breathless, blinding sojourn in a place
somewhere beyond the pale – perhaps in worlds similar to the
proposed 'supercurved' dimensions of theoretical physics – they
are once more drawn irresistibly down into the illusory world of
ordinary time. On the face of it, the situation might seem hopeless,
as indeed it was meant to, for the essence of the doctrine of
metempsychosis lies in the repeatedly expressed assertion that it is
in fact possible, through a systematic assimilation of harmonious
psychological values, to extricate ourselves from the futile, pathless
cycle of eternal recurrence.

As we shall see, in one form or another, this very principle is
expressed in all known religious doctrines. There is nothing
whatever fanciful or abstract about any one of them. They are codes
of survival, of 'redemption', and each describes in very clear and
precise terms a commonsense, *scientific* approach toward the
conscious acquisition of a constant or optimum state of being called
'individuality' – the indestructible mark of the true initiate. And this
optimum state of being, as the Greeks in particular were evidently
at such pains to demonstrate, is realized through the knowledge
and application of the unerring principles of esoteric music.

In early Greece, then, the hermetic movement flourished under its
new guise of 'science'. After the 'eccentric' Pythagoreans had
developed their various scientific interpretations of the sacred code
of Hermes, later Greek scholars quite naturally answered the
eternal call to awaken. Socrates, for example, was well-versed in
mathematics, sacred geometry and astronomy and is believed to
have received instruction from the esoteric order then existing on the

island of Samos. Renowned for his superior wisdom and emotional equilibrium, this great thinker was the supreme orator of his day, the mediator between the subjective world of the new, grosser, political consciousness and the objective world of harmony and pure Reason. His famous dictum, 'Know thyself', with its emphasis on cognition of the inner world of man, may well have been one of the chief inspirations behind the telling of a story which has since proved to be one of the greatest historical engimas of our times – Plato's legend of the lost continent of Atlantis.

The question as to whether or not this 'lost continent' ever existed has long been the subject of much speculation among archaeologists and historians. Theories about it are many and varied; and yet it would be true to say that practically every one of them has been principally concerned with the question of its existence as fact. To this end, all energies have quite naturally been directed toward locating the physical remains, the proof.

The entire Atlantis myth has been derived solely from Plato, who relates the story of its destruction in his dialogues *Timaeus* and *Critias*. According to the latter the information came from the statesman Solon, who allegedly obtained it direct from the priests of Ptolemaic Egypt. An Egyptian priest told Solon that the world had in fact seen many 'floods', but that the greatest of these – which is supposed to have occurred some nine thousand years before Plato took up his pen – was the one which destroyed the Atlantean civilization.

Latter-day interest in the story began in the 1880s, when Ignatius Donnelly, an American writer, published a book entitled *Atlantis, the Antediluvian World*. Donnelly claimed that Atlantis existed as a large continent lying in what is now the Atlantic Ocean, and that its kings and queens became the gods and goddesses of all later mythologies. He believed also that the fall of Atlantean society prior to the cataclysm was the origin of the legend of the Garden of Eden. More recently the American seer Edgar Cayce prophesied whilst in a state of hypnotic sleep that the remains of Atlantis – which he believed to have originally been a vast island stretching from the Sargasso Sea to the Azores – would eventually surface once again in the Caribbean Sea. In fact, certain structural remains have subsequently been discovered in and around that particular sea-bed, but there is no evidence to suggest that these are the 11,000-year-old remains of an antediluvian civilization.

Plato himself wrote that the continent existed 'beyond the twin pillars of Hercules', a reference commonly interpreted as meaning beyond the Straits of Gibraltar. More recently, however, the modern archaeologist has tended toward the theory that the legend in fact refers to the Minoan civilization on Santorini, an island near Crete, which was apparently destroyed by a tremendous volcanic explosion sometime around 1300 BC. There is a certain amount of circumstantial evidence to support this particular theory, both in the archaeological remains of the Minoan city itself and in the writings of Plato. But even if true, of course, the puzzle proper would still be unsolved, for one key question still remains. That is, assuming Plato was really writing about a civilization which existed in the Mediterranean Sea, where then, are the mysterious 'twin pillars' to be found? Clearly they are no ordinary 'pillars', for they have been allied to a very great and powerful mythological figure.

This question of the 'twin pillars' is possibly the key to the whole Atlantis myth. As for Santorini itself, this will be better left to the archaeologist, because the historicity of the lost continent is of lesser consequence than the significant but long overlooked fact that the legend itself exists. Furthermore, although it was written twenty-five hundred years ago, it still seems to capture the imagination of millions. (According to Colin Wilson there have been over two thousand books and articles written on the subject to date.)

From his use of the Lambda and numerous other Pythagorean symbols, it is obvious that Plato was as well-versed as his mentor in these new 'Greek' sciences. In fact, the whole body of Plato's writings is permeated with hermetic data, so it seems reasonable to suppose that the legend of Atlantis, with its all too-familiar universal appeal, is an essentially *hermetic* tale, designed to exist and to continually flow through the consciousness of man by a student of the grand old art of transcendental evolution. Conceivably, therefore, the citizen of this 'lost' world existing beyond the 'twin pillars of Hercules' (dualism?) is the inner man, the individual himself. If this is so, then the legendary Atlantis is still with us now, 'submerged' perhaps, but as real, in fact, as America or Asia. The problem is, as soon as we begin to think in purely logical or dualistic terms, the continent (literally, the main or whole body of the thing) actually does 'sink' below the level of one's ordinary modes of perception.

Atlantis, then, be it historical fact or intuitive portent of times to come, is possibly first and foremost an imperishable image of man's inner world, artistically drawn by Plato in his efforts to engender moments of contemplative speculation in the subjective, state-oriented minds of his peers and successors. And indeed, if the vast number of divergent theories on the subject is anything to judge by, then one would have to concede that in this at least he succeeded admirably.

As well as working to exercise his considerable influence over the greater Greek community, Plato also continued to redefine some of the more esoteric aspects of hermetism. Originally his ambitions had been political, but after witnessing the deplorable treatment of Socrates by the 'democratic' leaders of Greek society, he became convinced that there was no place for a man of conscience in such an arena. After the execution of Socrates he visited Egypt and Italy, and around 387 BC founded the famous Academy as a school for the systematic pursuit of philosophical and scientific research, which he presided over for the rest of his life.

One of the lesser-known art forms taught at this Academy was that of the literary craft of Gematria. This was the art of linking together individual letters with corresponding numbers in such a way that the compound value of whole words or phrases related one to the other, not only in a meaningful literary sense, but in mathematical and musical terms also. When the Greek version of the New Testament was subsequently compiled, much of the text of the Gospels and in particular the text of St John's Revelation were themselves written along the principles of Gematria, resulting in what is, as will later become evident, one of the most perfect pieces of literary art known to man.

The emergence of the hermetic tradition in Greece saw the building of the great temple known as the Heraion on the island of Samos. Construction began in 530 BC, but it wasn't completed until the third century BC. Little remains of it today. It was one of the seven wonders of the ancient world, dedicated to Hera, the patron deity of Samos who later became the celestial wife of Zeus, head of the Greek pantheon. According to legend, the diffused band of light in the night sky is the milk of Hera, squirted from her breast across the heavens – hence the well-known term Milky Way. In Greek esotericism this fundamentally feminine, passive symbol represented the cosmic note 'ti' of an evolutionary or tetradic octave. There are, in fact, exact parallels to this female transstellar symbol in the cosmologies of many of the world's religious doctrines – in particular the woman in heaven described in St John's Book of Revelation and the goddess Anahita of Zoroastrian origin, both of whom we shall be meeting later.

Also current in Samos at this time was the use of the canonical tradition of Egyptian sculpture and art, which existed in its original form right through to the time of the Renaissance. The system was based on a canon of proportions in which artistic portrayals of the physical body were divided into twenty-one parts. An ancient document known as the *Bibliotheca* tells how two well-known artists from the sixth century BC were commissioned by the people of Samos to execute a statue of Apollo. It was said that they made it in the Egyptian fashion by 'dividing the structure of the entire body into twenty-one parts and one fourth in addition'. The 'one fourth' is believed to refer to linear measurement – a fourth part of an Egyptian cubit – but one suspects that its real esoteric meaning can only be derived *musically*, in that it refers to the ultimate twenty-second division of the body, the transcendental fourth base of the completed triple-octave.

The hermetic chain of neo-Platonic days subsequently entered into another new stage of development. This was the age of logical cognition, Zoroaster's 'age of iron'. The seal of the Greek order was passed on, probably to Aristotle, the third of the great trio of Athenian adepts, who was unfortunate enough to have to contend, not only with a rapidly changing political panorama, but also with an extremely demanding and often difficult 'student' – Alexander the Great. Even so, from the compilation of the New Testament texts in accordance with the hermetic principles of Gematria, we can reasonably assume that Aristotle and his unnamed successors were to a large extent successful in their efforts to hand on the true esoteric principles of all Greek 'sciences'.

Traces of hermetic lore are, incidentally, easily identifiable in many of the legends of Greek mythology, which appear to have begun to be transmitted orally at around the time of Solomon. The legends and myths are numerous and complex and throughout history have suffered many different interpretations by scholars and mystics alike. Certain of them, however, are clearly hermetic in origin. The myth of the master musician Apollo and the nine Muses has been mentioned already. The story of the infamous Minotaur of the Labyrinth and the seven virgins is another classic example known by millions.

One of the most famous of all Greek legends is that of Orpheus, after whom the renowned Orphic Rites were named. The Platonic invention of the submerged continent may well have its original roots in this very legend, for Orpheus is said to have journeyed to the 'underworld' and there to have imparted his superior knowledge by playing a particularly special kind of music. The 'underworld' symbol is of course highly reminiscent of the submerged continent of later years, but in fact this whole story of the descent of a 'musician' into the lower realms of existence is nothing if not a precise, literal description of the method of exposition employed by all of the world's great spiritual leaders, who imparted their wisdom by example, by living, or 'playing out', a *harmonious* planetary existence.

CHAPTER NINE

Passion Play

Ye are from beneath; I am from above: ye are of this world; I
am not of this world.

Jesus, *John* 8.23

Four hundred years or so after the main activities of the hermetic
orders of Samos and Athens, there occurred another significant
turn of events in the development of Western civilization. This was
the appearance of Jesus Christ (from the Greek, *khristos* – 'the
anointed'), perhaps the most enigmatic of all revelationists, whose
overall influence upon the collective Western consciousness has
undoubtedly been the most far-reaching ever to have been generated.

In this chapter I intend to show that this unusually potent
psychological force was engendered in exactly the same way as
were the earlier influences of the Buddha and Zoroaster, Confucius
and Pythagoras; that is, by following to the letter the original
musical precepts of Thoth. Such was the 'science' as Jesus practised
and taught it and which is described in some detail in the Gospels.
But more of this later, after we have briefly examined the historical
development of Christianity as a whole.

Over the centuries, the movement initiated by Jesus has attracted
more criticism than possibly any other religion in the world. When
one considers the dubious activities of many of its self-proclaimed
representatives, past and present, it is easy to understand why,
although it must be said that the corruptive element so implicit in its

historical development is really a reflection of the peculiar nature of the evolving Western psyche and should not in itself be taken as an indictment of the Christian code. Real Christianity – the science of universal love, as practised and preached by Jesus himself – was relatively short-lived. It was born in turbulent times, in a densely populated, culturally unstable region of the earth which at that time was being governed by a new and forceful breed of politically conscious administrators. The Romans, however, were surprisingly unsuccessful in their efforts to suppress this new religion. For two hundred and fifty years they systematically persecuted its followers, but the movement continued to flourish until, finally, with the conversion of the Emperor Constantine in AD 312 Rome adopted Christianity as its formal religion.

Ironically this marked the beginning of the decline, the passing of 'Do' into 'ti', the birth of the formalized church of Rome. Inevitably the elected representatives of this new hierarchy now took on the reversed role of oppressor. With the backing of the Emperor Theodosius, the library of Alexandria was sacked and burnt down on the orders of the archbishop of Alexandria. Apparently he suspected the resident scholars of the library of practising 'alchemy' – which they probably did, though not necessarily of the kind he might have imagined, the transmutation of lead or mercury into gold. Mercury was associated with Hermes, the father of alchemy, a connection which strongly suggests that students who had at their disposal a vast library of rare books and manuscripts, many of them on Egyptian metaphysics, would also have been conversant with the sacred 'canon of proportions' and the principle of absolute harmony, the spiritual 'gold' of the ancient 'sons of kings'.

After this depressing act of wilful destruction, knowledge of any kind was considered evil, something to be suppressed at all costs, only to be replaced by the stagnant notion of demons or, worse still, the Devil himself waiting to ensnare those who dared carry anything other than the 'virtuous' cross of self-torment. Under such conditions, the Christian message might have faded altogether. But it didn't, in fact; it continued to be transmitted, though obviously in an adulterated form, leaving in its wake, on the one hand, a revitalized awareness of the 'Pythagorean' idea of the divinity of the human soul but, on the other, a confused trail of negativity which blazed unchecked for a thousand years and more.

It is this negative side of the Christian phenomenon to which Colin Wilson refers in his book *The Occult*, when he describes it as a disaster, an 'epidemic' rather than a religion, which appealed to the hysteria and ignorance of a gullible and superstitious people. His suggestion is that exoteric Christianity was the 'plague' itself, or at least the main cause of this ignorance. My own view is that it would probably be nearer the truth to say that man himself caused it, as indeed he always does, and that Christianity, having suffered several centuries of Romanization, had ceased to be an effective antidote. After all, ignorance and superstition were also the everyday companions of the natives of pre-Aryan India and, later, of the Persians in the time of Zoroaster. This is presumably the main reason why these great visionaries and teachers of old – including Jesus – went to such pains to make their 'immaculate' presences felt, to show man how to lift his consciousness up out of the mists of time and so cure him of his earthbound ills. (When Jesus was challenged about his association with tax-barons and 'sinners', he replied, 'It is not the healthy people that need a doctor but the sick.' – *Mark* 2.17, New English Bible)

So the early Roman censorship and oppression, the barbarian incursions and the subsequent Dark Ages, the ill-conceived Crusades, the intolerance and brutality of conquistador 'missionaries' and inquisitor-generals – all this would probably have occurred anyway, irrespective of the dominant religion of the age. The Romans would still have colonized Europe and Asia Minor, their successors would almost certainly have discovered and 'civilized' the Americas, Gnostic and Kabbalistic societies would still have been forced underground by some formalized hierarchy in pursuit of absolute power. Whether or not one of the prevailing religions other than Christianity might have fared better through all this we shall never know; but it is doubtful. The earlier Orphic and Dionysian mysteries were still popular in the Graeco-Roman era, as was the worship of Helios (the sun), or Re, its Egyptian equivalent, or the Apollo of the Pythagoreans; but many if not all of these 'religions' had by this time degenerated into the practice of empty ritual and orgiastic rites, which bore little or no resemblance to the original hermetic blueprint upon which they were founded.

As for Christianity itself, whether one regards its appearance as a good thing or a bad thing, it was obviously the religion most suited to the conditions then existing, and to the conditions which arose during subsequent centuries of erratic social development in the West. Today its influence exists in a somewhat diffused form, manifesting itself largely through the simplistic fundamentalism of the Billy Graham type of evangelism, or through the works of divers and often unimaginative theologians; but for over nineteen hundred years, through the dense gloom and ignorance of the Dark and Middle Ages, through the tremendous social and religious upheavals of sixteenth-century Europe, and the subsequent rise of positivistic science, Darwinism and the crass materialism of the industrial revolution – through all this the more positive aspects of Christian influence have survived every form of suppression and corruption imaginable.

That there *is* a positive side to the Christian phenomenon is a fact that no serious observer of the history of Western civilization will deny. As the New Testament scholar C. H. Dodd remarks of the early movement in his book *The Founder of Christianity*, 'It is impossible to conceive what would have come out of the chaos of the Dark Age without the church.' The church was the institution which effectively bridged the gap between the old Graeco-Roman civilization and the new one, heralded by the Italian renaissance. Not only did it preserve the use of Latin and maintain the rudiments of law and order, it also encouraged the revival of agriculture, practical craftsmanship and architecture; and through its vast network of monastic communities, it provided the basis of learning and education.

The Christian church thus had two faces: one which resembled in every way the Devil of its own creation and which looked on and encouraged the manic burning of books and heretics; another which, in addition to preaching the Gospels, saw to it that the people at least knew how to fulfil their more practical needs. (The former visage – the face of the Devil – was not, incidentally, a new invention. It was simply a variation on the earlier Zoroastrian theme, misconstrued by later Christian interpreters, which portrayed the negative impulses of man as being manifestations of the demon Ahriman. In this respect it is worth noting that there are other key similarities between the religion of the three wise men of the Nativity and the one later founded by the child to whom they went to pay homage. Each had its Messiah, each prophesied a

Second Coming, each had its own interpretation of heaven and hell.).

Although the church of Rome did indeed have its many imperfections and consistently gave cause for universal condemnation, it is a curious fact that, apart from early Roman and Jewish propaganda, there has been rarely a word spoken anywhere in criticism of Jesus personally, or of the way he conducted himself during his lifetime. Muslims have the greatest respect for him, as anyone who has read the Koran will know. In Orthodox Jewish tradition, the worst that has ever been said of him is that he was executed because he practised sorcery and was leading Israel astray – a rather vague accusation, but one which grudgingly acknowledges Jesus as having been something of a magus, a man who, if capable of seducing a whole nation, must have possessed unusually strong psychic powers. To the rest of the non-Christian world, Jesus is regarded either with respect or indifference; but if any intelligent observer of human nature, of whatever political or cultural persuasion, were familiarized with his life as it is portrayed in the Gospels, he or she would be very hard pressed to discredit the things he said and did. This is an important point, because it touches on the real reason for the otherwise inexplicable resilience of the Christian movement, which is that it is the person of the founder himself, not the church, whence the real power emanates. Without Jesus, even if the church's dogma had been constructed from broadly the same precepts expounded by him, there would have been little or no trace of Christianity today. Like the Greek mysteries, or the later Roman cult of Mithras, it would soon have been relegated to the realms of history or mythology.

But as we have seen, this did not happen; the life of Jesus was far too profound a series of events for it to be forgotten so easily. And there are millions alive today whose beliefs are testimony to this strange and remarkable fact.

Thus the part played by the church in the development of Western culture is significant in itself, but there is a whole spectrum of wider influence still emanating from the source – from Jesus himslf – whose positive effects upon the human race are virtually incalculable. Consider the countless numbers of genuine Christian saints and mystics whose lives have been devoted to keeping his memory alive, the unending stream of creative artistry inspired by the Nativity and the Passion, the thousands upon thousands of chapels, churches and magnificent Gothic cathedrals which have been built in his name. And all this before we even begin to consider the more subtle, unquantifiable effects upon us all – even upon atheists and non-Christians – of his common-sense doctrine of universal love and compassion.

Surely, therefore, even the most hostile critic of the church itself would have to agree that the impressions left behind in space and time by this young Jewish individual are some of the most potent ever to have been created. And this all-powerful potency, remember, was generated to such an astonishing degree in only thirty-three short years.

Like the Buddha, Jesus was a historical figure. The Gospels of Matthew and Luke both state that he was born in Bethlehem in Judaea, the first-born of his mother whose name was Mary. According to Matthew, he was born sometime before the death of Herod in the spring of 4 BC, but Luke places at the time of the imperial census in Palestine, which occurred around AD 6. Joseph, his father, or foster father, appears to have passed away by the time Jesus's mission began, but there are references in Corinthians, Galatians and Mark to several brothers (James, Joses, Judas and Simon) and sisters (unnamed).

By all accounts, Jesus seems to have been something of a problem to his family. In the early days of his ministry they were convinced that he was going insane and attempted to restrain him. At the same time, however, there were many who held a very different view and who treated him with a marked degree of deference. Such people frequently consulted him on philosophical and religious matters and addressed him as 'Rabbi' or 'Teacher'. This suggests that some part of his undocumented early life was probably spent in a detailed study of the religion and history of his people. Certainly the evidence in the Gospels of his deep understanding of the Old Testament supports this.

The exact dates of his ministry are unknown. It is thought to have started after he had been initiated by John the Baptist sometime between AD 27 and AD 29, so it seems likely that prior to this he spent some time in close association with John and his work in

Judaea and neighbouring Peraea. It was allegedly at the moment of his baptism (clearly a passive, receptive state of being) that Jesus, who had previously acknowledged the authenticity of John's work, became aware that he had been assigned to a destiny beyond the mission of John, saying that he had been chosen by God to proclaim a message greater even than that of Israel's.

According to Mark, the Christian mission as we know it began in and around Galilee with the proclamation (*Mark* 1.14–15) that the 'New Age' had dawned. Immediately Jesus began calling people to join him as members of a new brotherhood. The Galilean episode marked a period of growing popularity with ordinary people, who possibly looked upon Jesus's unique acts of benevolence as being a refreshing change from the usual, grasping ways of the common, law-abiding social animal. The sojourn in Galilee ended with the mysterious feeding of the five thousand men (*Mark* 6.30–44). This particular story, as we shall see, carries a most significant message; but whether true or not, the fact that it had been told at all clearly reflects Christ's rapid increase in popularity at that time.

Obviously this unexpected popularity wasn't universal. Cynical and suspicious eyes followed Jesus's every movement, especially those of the scribes and Pharisees, who were more than a little put out by his attitude toward their legalistic interpretations of Mosaic law. Not only that, Jesus consistently displayed what was considered by many to be an unhealthy disregard for this law. He drank on the Sabbath, feasted during the fasts, cursed the usurers in the Temple and unceasingly pointed out the inherent weaknesses of the bourgeoisie. They in turn responded by calling him, among other things, 'a gluttonous man, and a winebibber, a friend of publicans and sinners' (*Luke* 7.34).

Toward the end of Lent, the mission arrived first at the ancient city of Jericho, and then Bethany, where the raising of Lazarus took place. This would have been just prior to the period we now know as Easter Week, which began with the procession on Palm Sunday and ended, exactly seven days later, on the Sunday of the Resurrection. On arrival in Jerusalem, Jesus and his disciples made their way directly to the Temple, where they stayed for a brief period before returning to Bethany for the night. Next day Jesus returned to the capital, to the Temple precincts, and there began his notorious public criticism of the official representatives of the

Jewish religion. From this moment on events moved quickly. The priests duly convened a meeting of the Sanhedrin, the great council, headed by the high priest Joseph Caiaphas, at which it was decided that Jesus was too much of a threat to them to be left at large. It is accepted by everyone that he eventually appeared in the court of the Roman procurator Pontius Pilate, and that he was subsequently crucified.

Contemporary Roman accounts of these events say that Jesus was executed as a rebel, a nationalist Zealot, and that such a charge was both unexpected and embarrassing for his followers, who were supposedly demoralized by his sudden and ignominious death. This may be true with regard to his wider circle of followers who, as Mark reports, were fearful when the march into the capital began: 'They were on the road, going up to Jerusalem, Jesus leading the way; and the disciples were filled with awe, while those who followed behind were afraid.' (*Mark* 10.32 New English Bible). In the King James Version Mark goes on to say that Jesus then '. . . took again the twelve, and began to tell them what things should happen unto him'. In fact, Jesus spent a great deal of time and effort schooling his disciples during those final days. Thus whilst his wider circle of followers may well have been mortified by the dramatic turn of events which culminated in Jesus's execution, his inner circle were fully prepared; they knew exactly what was going to happen and what they must afterwards do.

As for Jesus himself, he knew perfectly well that, as a direct result of his extraordinary activities, the gates of Jerusalem would automatically snap like teeth behind him. Indeed he was counting on it. He was a man with a special mission, the successful outcome of which depended entirely on his suffering an agonizing and brutal death in full view of everyone.

We can't pretend to know exactly how such a man's mind worked, but it is clear that Jesus was prepared to go through hell to gain the attention of his contemporaries, who in his view were spiritually bankrupt. Palestinian society was at that time in serious disarray and Israel itself had been repeatedly plundered and torn apart during the first millennium BC, so it is hardly surprising that the original hermetic teachings of the elders should have suffered a certain amount of neglect, remembered only in times of great personal crisis, danger and so forth. Thus the people had effectively forsaken Israel. Jesus's one and only 'violent' act – that of overturning the tables of the moneychangers in the holy Temple precincts – shows that he personally viewed the situation with abject disdain. Something was drastically amiss: the prized harmony of the Golden Age, having not been, as Confucius would have put it, 'modulated by ritual', had been lost yet again.

This inherent lack of social and spiritual wellbeing would have been due partly, as I have said, to the state of Israel's earlier misfortunes of war, but also to the fact that Roman rule in the Middle East was at first one of intellectual intolerance, a temporary triumph of the sword over the pen. After the partial destruction and looting of the Alexandrian library during Cleopatra's reign, a sizable store of Greek literature perished or was removed, along with many other works of Babylonian, Persian and Egyptian origin. Subsequently the mainstream of hermetic influence disappeared even further underground; knowledge itself became increasingly more 'occult', the hidden property of Essenes, Gnostics and other such esoteric societies. But in the exoteric world, there was only 'cacophony'. Conditions of social existence had by now become so negatively charged that the hermetic associates of Christ, inspired of course by Jesus himself, decided that they had to take some kind of drastic remedial action. Remember, these people were genuine revelationists, dedicated individuals who viewed the whole scenario of human evolution on a grand scale, rather as if it were a real-life musical extravaganza. But it was a musical which had lost its edge: the tunes were old, the notes were flat and the performers were way out of step. In hermetic terminology one could say that the characteristic resonance – the 'pitch' – of this collective psychic medium had degenerated to such an extent that it now required the additional impetus of a certain and unique kind of external 'shock' to lift it once more into the higher realms of objective existence. In other words, in a very real sense, the general populace was asleep, unconscious, steeped in dreams and subjective fantasies. The spirited and oft-quoted call 'Awake! Watch! for ye know not the day nor the hour!' (*Matthew* 25.13) is a direct allusion to these 'catatonic' tendencies of the undisciplined human mind. But in fact, the Gospels and the Book of Revelation are full of such warnings to the common man; and Palestinian society is consistently portrayed as having been a degenerate entity, with Jerusalem existing as some kind of biblical red-light zone inhabited by whole tribes of cheats, fools and hypocrites – a far cry from Eden to be sure.

The subsequent sequence of events following the spectacular disruption at the Temple in Jerusalem has proved difficult to document with any real accuracy. Many scholars have tried to piece together a coherent factual account of Jesus's last days, but whilst attention to the smallest detail may be important from a purely historical point of view, the essential eight-day format of the story is what really counts. The Passion was clearly outlined in the Gospels as a week-long event as is to this day re-enacted as such in churches and schools the world over. As we shall see, it is this distinctive 'octave' format of the narrative wherein lies the real secret of the universal appeal of Christianity, for the Passion itself, regarded by most serious scholars as the kernel of all Christian belief, was a hermetic production from beginning to end, a harmoniously composed sequence of human activity orchestrated strictly according to the scientific principles of esoteric music. Before looking at the overall 'musical' pattern of Jesus's movements, however, it will help better to understand the unique events of Easter Week if we first follow the story line through, paying particular attention to the final three days.

We know Jesus went from Bethany to Jerusalem, allegedly on the back of a donkey, a quadruped, and that when he arrived he immediately set about actively stirring up trouble. He was subsequently arrested, tried, sentenced and then crucified at the 'third hour' of the sixth day, our Good Friday. By the 'sixth hour' it was dark. At the 'ninth hour' Jesus allegedly uttered his famous cry, 'Eloi, Eloi, lama sabachthani?' – and then he died. If he had not died then, the Romans, mindful of the local custom, would have despatched him by clubbing him to death – Jewish tradition demanded that all activities, including burials, had to cease by the beginning of the Sabbath.

One of Jesus's followers, a wealthy man called Joseph of Arimathea, went immediately to Pilate and asked for permission to remove the body. This being duly granted, he took Jesus's mutilated body, had it wrapped in a shroud and then placed in his own tomb in a nearby private garden. For the rest of Friday evening, the whole of Saturday, and possibly the early hours before dawn on Sunday, the body is said to have lain still in the tomb.

Then comes the most controversial part of the narrative, which says that, on the third day after his death, Jesus, like Lazarus only days before in Bethany, came back to life.

There have been endless arguments about the literal truth of the Resurrection, but whether the events actually transpired as they are described or not, we are asked to believe that they did, i.e. that Jesus rose from the dead.

All four Gospels state that, on the Sunday morning after the Friday on which Jesus died, his tomb was found to be empty. Luke says that two of the women who first discovered the empty sepulchre (possibly Mary Magdalene and the 'other Mary' mentioned in *Matthew* 28.1) subsequently met Jesus on the road some distance from Jerusalem and shared their food with him. They later walked with him on to Bethany and, while Jesus blessed the women, he was mysteriously 'parted from them, and carried up into heaven' (*Luke*, 24.51).

The other Gospels differ concerning the identity and number of witnesses to Jesus's miraculous reappearance, but all of them assert that this actually happened. Naturally the logical mind balks at such a proposition. But possibly this is because the Gospel narratives were designed specifically to have such an effect. A complacent, unchallenged mind tends to sleep on, but a mind that is in some way disturbed, say, by being confronted with an illogical fact, inevitably wakes up a little. Thus the assertion that Jesus (and indeed Lazarus) actually did come alive again is so apparently emphatic that even the rationalistic nonbeliever can occasionally experience a certain amount of disquiet or even wonder at the thought of such a possibility. One must admit that the story is certainly out of the ordinary, but quite apart from the miraculous Resurrection itself, there are also other, telltale, illogical features of the Passion narrative worthy of comment.

Consider, for example, the stated reason for Jesus's extraordinary actions. Practically every lay Christian knows that he stepped out into the exoteric world and offered himself up to be put to death in the most terrible fashion conceivable; and that he did this for the sins of his people. Clearly there is a paradox here of almost gross proportions, for why should any man do such a thing for the sake of an indeterminate population of careless miscreants, when lawfully, or logically, it might well have been his persecutors up there on that cross?

To answer this question we must first try to understand what exactly Jesus meant when he referred to the 'sins' of man. Standard Christian preaching generally contains plenty of oblique references to sin and the wages thereof, but beyond quoting parrot-fashion the Ten Commandments, or fragments of the Sermon on the Mount, theologians rarely attempt to define our 'trespasses', let alone explain in common-sense terms how the brutal crucifixion of a single individual could possibly help to eradicate their negative effects. Nowadays the concept of sin has a somewhat outdated ring to it. Over the centuries it has inevitably acquired a string of vaguely related definitions, most of them being of a social or moral nature. But morality, as any social scientist knows, changes with time. What is acceptable today may be inappropriate tomorrow and positively criminal in due course. Therefore morality as such is very often incidental to the kind of transgression that Jesus was evidently so concerned about. Speaking objectively, as he always did, we can say that real sins – i.e. the 'seven deadly' ones – arise from those thoughts and actions of a human being which effectively impede the process of his or her own personal evolution. Anything else we may choose to do is by the way, defined by the arbitrary strictures of social law and so not strictly relevant to the essential Christian message.

The point I am trying to make here is that 'sins' in themselves are never performed or committed consciously. By their very nature, they cannot be; which means that any 'guilt' one might feel about them must inevitably sink into the hidden depths of the subconscious. Therefore guilt lies deep; it is a burden most of us carry throughout our lives without ever being aware of it. Yet somehow, if mankind is to evolve in a fully harmonious way, this guilt has to be made to surface. Some kind of impetus, some special metaphysical component is required to enable the mind to release, to realize this hidden sense of guilt before it congeals into spiritual lead.

As I said earlier, the necessary impetus in the first century AD came from the effects arising from the production of the Passion Play, an eight-day, deliberately planned work of musical revelation, written and performed by the greatest exponents of living art the world has ever known.

Given the obvious gravity of the situation, the sheer intensity or 'passion' of it, we can reasonably suppose that this strange and in many ways awesome act of personal sacrifice was rather more than a desperate *cri de coeur*. Originally intended to have a direct, positive influence over the maximum number of people possible, the whole production was, in effect, an extremely skilful piece of psychological 'surgery', performed by expert metaphysicians upon the ill-formed body of the collective social consciousness; a world-shattering blow to man's newly discovered and much-cherished rule of logic. For the innocent party to genuinely forgive such terrible deeds in this all-wise and compassionate way was an incomprehensible act. No wonder people looked twice at it. Normally the guilty were seen fit only to be punished, and severely so. This was the law; it was the way of society as it then stood, the logical conclusion interpreted and subjectively determined for the good of all by the possessors of political and social power. But these were laws which, quite naturally, had been twisted and distorted to accommodate the secular needs of a nonexistent (in the harmonious, objective sense) society.

So it was that the creative impetus of centuries past, generated by the great revelationists of China, Persia, India and Greece, subsequently decreased in pitch, or in quality of resonance, to the dualistic level of the logician. Possibly Aristotle's considerable influence over late Greek philosophical thought played a significant part in this decline, although virtually all of the ageing hierarchies whose influences still permeated Palestinian society at that time would have been contributing in their own way. At any rate, by the time Jesus appeared, the spirit of 'divine' revelation was conspicuous only by its absence. And if we continue to look upon the spheres of human activity in Palestine as being essentially musically structured phenomena, then we can say that this latent or recessive human condition, in being the passive coordinate of the first creative (or active) force of revelation, marked the time and place of an 'interval' in a greater, fundamental octave of evolutionary resonance, as it decreased in quality on its progression down through the ages. In short, a *semitone* was required. Furthermore, in order to be fully effective, this semitone had to be composed entirely of hermetic data. It had to be one hundred and one per cent harmonious, to be created at the right time and in the right place, at precisely the right psychological pitch, and upon the very soundest of all foundations.

The semitone, remember, is a harmonious concentration of resonating energy and form which, having been generated into play by the 'musician', subsequently becomes the medium through which two fundamentally different coordinates, or notes, may be united.

The Passion of Jesus Christ was just such a phenomenon. It was an imperishable metaphysical tetrad, a semitone of human activity, a harmoniously composed octave of psychological energy and form which mirrored exactly the omnipotent forces constantly at play in the world of nature:

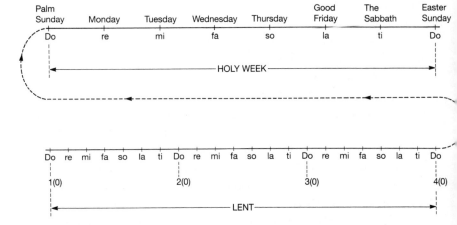

The rest, as they say, is history. The sacred tetrad had been 'squared' like never before, and the harmonious psychological semitone generated thereby sounded long and deeply within the passive, subconscious minds of the people. The greater octave of evolutionary resonance then proceeded, despite the innumerable and petty inquisitions of man, in a straight line; that is, across time, centuries and millennia of it.

The entire tapestry of symbolism created by the Christian school is ablaze with images which are clearly of a hermetic nature. The message of the Trinity is self-evident: it is simply another variation on the original theme of the three aspects of one reality. The four Archangels are also of hermetic design, as indeed are the Four Horsemen of the Apocalypse in Revelation (6.1–8), or the four angels bound in the river Euphrates who prepared themselves to sound the death knell of the 'third part of men' (9.14–15). Like the four Noble Truths of the Buddha, the four Hsiang of the *I Ching*, or the story of the four decades of exile prior to the creation of Israel, they are precise, psychical or metaphysical base-notes echoing in the passive recesses of the subconscious mind. They form the 'sound' base upon which, and from which, the tetrad of psychological resonance can develop – an intuitive aid to the process of assimilation of the four key Gospel texts. This would denote the preparatory stage of Christian initiation, the founding of the 'rock' upon which the dedicated adherent must build.

Now there is also the question of Christ's age at the time of the Crucifixion. If the Passion Play was indeed written and performed by genuine adepts, then it seems unlikely that the number thirty-three should have been simply an arbitrary choice.

It is important to understand that to the ancients – particularly those versed in Pythagorean and Essene mysticism – numbers themselves, like the symbols of the sacred art of geometry, were regarded as entities in their own right, each being possessed with its own distinct individuality. Ten, for example, the esoteric symbol of the tetrad, was regarded as a 'perfect' number, not only because it is the sum of all the numbers one to four (the sum of the base-notes), but also because, as a symbol of esoteric musical notation, it can be further divided into twenty-two inner notes. Certain numbers, therefore, were looked upon as having several different acknowledged facets, some of which projected logical geometrical or mathematical themes, others which carried with them wider, symbolic or hermetic connotations.

In the same way the symbol represented by Christ's age at the time of his death can be taken not only at face value (i.e. thirty-three), but also as an esoteric expression of the union of two sets of three. And three, as we know, is itself an expression of the first law of nature, the trinity. In fact, this combined image of two sets of three is by no means unique. The *I Ching* hexagram, Solomon's six-pointed seal, the lesser branches of the Hebraic menorah – all are composed of two complementary trinities. Possibly the most descriptive example of this particular hermetic format is to be found in the above-mentioned *Book of Changes*, in which two trinities – the two trigrams of each hexagram – together combine to produce one of the sixty-four realizable possibilities contained within the book. But then, what of the other sixty-three possibilities? What of the whole phenomenon?

To find the answer to this question we need to look once again at the number and sequence of the pebbles of the Pythagorean tetrad:

Note that the third stage of development of the tetrad is marked by the placing of two pebbles, the Same and the Other of Platonic invention. Now, in order to have reached this stage, the three interacting orders of energy and form of the second level must have achieved a certain optimum potential. But how can this be, when the optimum manifestation should logically be represented by the single pebble at the apex of the pyramid?

If we count the number of pebbles used to denote the first two stages in the development of the tetrad – •ˑ•ˑ•ˑ• – we see there are seven; and the seventh stage in a diagrammatic expression of harmonious musical notation would be as shown:

1	2	3	4	5	6	7*	8	9	10
Do	re	mi	∗	fa	so	la	ti	∗	Do
1	2	3		4	5	6*	7		8

– the sixth fundamental note, or Good Friday of the eight-day Passion Play, the day Christ died.

So the three interacting orders of energy and form, 'sensations', 'emotions' and 'perceptions', comprising the psychological presence of this crucified individual will have combined harmoniously at the evolutionary note 'la' to generate a transcendental signal up into the next scale of development – the third stage of the tetrad denoted by the said two pebbles. One of these pebbles, number eight in succession from the first base-note, represents the evolving tripart phenomenon itself (the first 'three') and is designated by the seventh fundamental note, 'ti'. The 'other' pebble, the ninth (the second 'three') represents the final semitone interval which unites the evolving series of notes with the ultimate note 'Do' at the top of the scale.

This third stage therefore implies some kind of union of the evolving scale of resonance with an external, supernatural intervention, i.e. the introduction of a fully harmonious, 'universal' semitone. And if the evolving tetrad is the initiate himself, this must mean that at the eighth stage (the seventh, passive note 'ti'), his own individual efforts are here complete. He is, in the earthly sense, 'dead', totally passive. The remaining interval between the initiate at this stage and his ultimate objective will be filled by the greater, omnipotent forces of nature existing beyond the limits described by our ordinary modes of perception – in the subconscious realms, as it were, where intuition enters into play.

And what is the nature of this compatible trinity? What is there in nature that exists beyond the time-scale of man? What is there in nature that could provide energy enough for the evolving tetrad to 'square' itself?

The answer, at least according to the esoteric content of the Old Testament stories of Noah and his successors, is of course the rainbow, the covenant – or light itself, the finest order of materiality discernible by the senses, the vehicle, as it were, of all man's perceptions. Light, in other words, is the fully harmonious, universal medium through which the degrees of psychological resonance at the evolutionary note 'ti' may proceed toward their main objective. (This suggestion, though scientifically unprovable, is more than tentative and will be outlined in more detail in a later chapter devoted to the question of light.)

But for the present, and with regard to the true significance of the thirty-three-year life span of the enigmatic Son of Man, Christ was saying, in effect, that at the cosmic note 'ti' in our octave of personal evolution, when the first 'three', (the inner triad, the sanctuary that is below) is ready to harmonize with the second 'three' (the outer triad, the sanctuary that is above), then our earthly existence has truly been fulfilled. And to show us all clearly and precisely that this is so, this remarkable individual voluntarily gave up his planetary existence after exactly thirty-three years. Had it been thirty-two, or thirty-four, or twenty-nine, an overall image of perfect symbolic symmetry would never have been achieved. It had to be thirty-three. The work demanded that this symbol be transmitted perpetually across time. And so it was.

One other prominent symbol of the Passion narrative which is of particular interest is the number twelve, the number of disciples under the direct tutelage of Christ who forgathered for a final meeting at the Last Supper. All were present on that fateful evening, so it seems reasonable to suppose that the lasting image of a master and twelve subordinates was created for a definite purpose. This is in fact the case, as will become evident in the following section devoted to a musical analysis of certain of the Gospel texts. Traditionally one of the twelve – the infamous Judas Iscariot – is regarded as having been a traitor. Obviously, whether true or not, this alleged treachery can be neither proved nor disproved, but one can't help but feel that the idea of someone of the intellectual and spiritual capacity of Christ being *betrayed* by one of his closest companions – and for only a few paltry pieces of silver – has an altogether familiar, 'illogical' ring to it. In fact it specifically states in the Gospels that Christ knew that this was going to happen:

> . . . but woe to that man by whom the Son of man is betrayed! good were it for that man if he had never been born.
>
> *Mark* 14.21

Remember we are speaking now of real, living art. The finest. Every scene, every action, every spoken and recorded word was planned from the very beginning. At the Last Supper the final sacred pacts were made and the ill-fated twelfth man, having received his terrible instructions, simply did what was asked of him. So by allowing himself to be branded as a traitor and dying, voluntarily, with a name that would forever linger on the tongues of men in the form of a curse, Judas Iscariot was undoubtedly one of the most devoted and selfless initiates of all time. His was a classic example of the supreme sacrifice, surpassed only by his own master's incredible act of self-denial.

And he asked them, How many loaves have ye? And they said, Seven.

And He commanded the people to sit down on the ground: and he took the seven loaves, and gave thanks, and brake, and gave to his disciples to set before them; and they did set them before the people.

And they had a few small fishes: and .he blessed, and commanded to set them also before them.

So they did eat, and were filled: and they took up of the broken meat that was left seven baskets.

And they that had eaten were about four thousand.

Mark 8.5–9

The Vesica – the sign of the fish – was especially influential at the beginning of the Christian era, but it had been respected from the earliest times as a symbol of the sacred marriage, when the spiritual world of 'essences' unites with the lower world of material phenomena. It was described in geometrical terms by Plato as the symbol produced through the interpenetration of two circles:

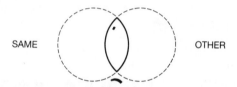

So the fish symbolizes the mediating principle between two opposing coordinates; in musical terms, the interval between two fundamentally different concentrations of resonance.

The preceding passage from Mark thus appears to be making reference to the fact that the seven 'loaves' (the seven fundamental notes of the given octave) were harmoniously composed, the necessary semitones between each of the fundamental notes having been 'filled' by conscious intervention on the part of Jesus, who, as was said, 'blessed' the small fishes also. So the harmonious sevenfold octave like this:

– is, in reality, a consciously composed tetrad; that is, an evolutionary octave of energy and form in which the two notes 'mi' and 'ti' already contain the additional degrees of resonance necessary for them to evolve up into the notes 'fa' and 'Do' respectively, thus:

And, as we earlier established from our discussion on Pythagorean law, this symbol of harmonious musical notation can be taken to be comprised of a chain of nine intervals or links, three sets of three links each:

And, from the rule of the first law of three, we know that this chain of links is, in fact, comprised of three interpenetrating orders of energy and form, so:

– which same orders of energy and form, according to the second law of nature, are themselves composed within, and transmute one to another without, as octaves. We thus have one fundamental octave and three subordinate ones:

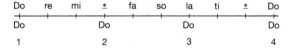

– with four 'sound' bases.

Now each of these three subordinate octaves – again according to the first law of nature – is also composed within of three interpenetrating orders of energy and form:

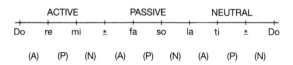

And, according to the second law of course, these three inner orders of energy and form are also composed within, and transmute one to another without, as octaves. We thus have a sum total of nine subordinate octaves:

```
Do          Do          Do          Do
+   +   +   +   +   +   +   +   +   +
Do  Do  Do  Do  Do  Do  Do  Do  Do  Do
```

So the first three subordinate octaves comprising the original fundamental tetrad ultimately become inwardly squared into nine. Nine octaves, of course, from the first base-note 'Do' to the last, give a total of precisely sixty-four notes · the square of the constant, eight.

Now we know from the dictum of Hermes/Thoth, 'As above, so below', that when a given phenomenon (in the case of the parable of the seven loaves and few small fishes this would be the sequence of events enacted by Christ and his disciples) is harmoniously composed within, it subsequently acquires the supernatural power, through the square of the constant, to generate a transcendental influence without: that is, into the greater scale 'above'. Consequently when the tetrad is 'squared', the four sound basenotes upon which the first three subordinate octaves are constructed may be said to expand accordingly and to subsequently 'fill' everything existing within their given sphere of influence – including that is, 'the multitude'.

The last reference of this particular parable, 'And they took up of the broken meat that was left seven baskets', refers to that which remained after this demonstration of Jesus's miraculous powers had been completed. The loaves themselves were no more. All that remained were the seven fragmented, or disharmonious, concentrations of resonance: a natural, involving octave.

. . . he [Jesus] saith unto them, Why reason ye, because ye have no bread? perceive ye not yet, neither understand? have ye your heart yet hardened?

Having eyes, see ye not? and having ears, hear ye not? and do ye not remember?

When I brake the five loaves among five thousand, how many baskets full of fragments took ye up? They say unto him, Twelve.

Mark 8.17–19

The story of the breaking of the five loaves is well known, but its true esoteric significance has yet to be explained by the conventional theologian. Once again, however, if one applies as criteria for analysis the original precepts of Hermes, then the whole of the parable in question becomes clear. What we see, in fact, is an extremely artistic, wholly accurate description, in symbolized form, of the Sacred Constant itself.

The whole story is 'composed' of the following key pieces of hermetic imagery: the five 'loaves', the two 'fishes' and the twelve baskets full of 'fragments' left after five thousand men had eaten and were 'filled'. Upon close examination we find that from these three fundamental symbols it is possible to describe yet another aspect of the Pythagorean octave, as important, if not more so, as even the sacred tetrad for, according to the musical theory of the first philosopher himself, the natural (i.e. involving) octave is actually composed, not of seven, not of ten, not of twenty-two, but of *twenty* basic divisions. That is, between each of the seven fundamental notes of a natural octave, there are considered to be not one but two semitones each, except between the notes 'mi–fa' and 'ti–Do', where there is only one semitone, one missing from each. (Which means, of course, that the tetrad itself, with its seven fundamental notes and two extra semitones, is in fact a shorthand version of the real process of esoteric musical notation.)

We thus have a natural, twenty-note scale looking like this:

1	2	3	4	5	6	7	8	9	10	11	12	13	14	15	16	17	18	19	20
Do	*	*	re	*	*	mi	*	fa	*	*	so	*	*	la	*	*	ti	*	Do

But this twenty-note scale, in lacking one semitone apiece between the notes 'mi–fa' and 'ti–Do', would in fact be fundamentally disharmonious. In reality, therefore, this octave, being natural, would not *evolve* (in a straight line), but would *involve*, like so:

128

'. . . and do ye not remember?' Christ must here have been referring to the two 'fishes', perhaps the most fondly remembered Piscean symbols in the whole of history. Is this not true? Once heard of, who could ever forget those two altogether remarkable 'fishes'? Evidently the authors of this text intended that we, today, should never do so. And possibly the reason we do still remember this ancient, all-wise parable is simply that the symbols or 'signals' of which it is composed are harmonious in every way – they are 'hermetically sealed'. Thus it was that the Vesica, the ancient symbol of the sacred marriage between heaven and earth, was used in this particular text to denote the two notes 'mi' and 'ti' of the octave. Christ was reminding his followers of the absolute necessity of introducing the two additional semitones at exactly the point in time and space where the note 'mi' begins to evolve into 'fa', and where the note 'ti' begins to evolve into 'Do'. So, with the aid of the two Vesicas, the *natural* twenty-note octave is miraculously transformed into a *supernatural, twenty-two*-note expression of pure harmony:

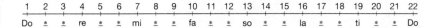

It is *pi*. And it is composed of five fundamental notes ('loaves'):

– two especially composed notes ('fishes'):

And: '. . . how many baskets full of fragments took ye up?' That is, when the tetrad had been 'squared' and the five thousand men had been 'filled' (no doubt with awe) – how many semitones remained? Answer, *twelve*; precisely the number necessary to complete the major Pythagorean octave being described:

CHAPTER TEN

Decoding Revelation

The New Testament is as old as the hills.

Mayavitch

The following texts are taken from the Revelation of St John the Divine:

And behold, a throne was set in heaven, and one sat on the throne.

Revelation 4.2

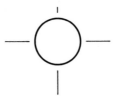

And out of the throne proceeded lightnings and thunderings and voices: and there were seven lamps of fire burning before the throne, which are the seven Spirits of God.

Revelation 4.5

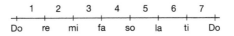

And round about the throne were four and twenty seats: and upon the seats I saw four and twenty elders sitting, clothed in white raiment; and they had on their heads crowns of gold.

Revelation 4.4

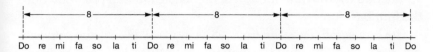

And before the throne there was a sea of glass like unto crystal: and in the midst of the throne, and round about the throne, were four beasts full of eyes before and behind.

And the first beast was like a lion, and the second beast like a calf, and the third beast had a face as a man, and the fourth beast was like a flying eagle.

And the four beasts had each of them six wings about him, and they were full of eyes within.

Revelation 4.6–8

LION	CALF	MAN	EAGLE
Do	Do	Do	Do
1 ti	1 ti	1 ti	1 ti
2 la	2 la	2 la	2 la
3 so	3 so	3 so	3 so
4 fa	4 fa	4 fa	4 fa
5 mi	5 mi	5 mi	5 mi
6 re	6 re	6 re	6 re
Do	Do	Do	Do

As we can see, the whole of St John's introductory text is a brilliantly orchestrated cover version of the age-old Holy of Holies. It is a perfect cosmological description of the tetrad.

At the apex of the pyramid is the Father: the absolute, full, harmonious 'Do'. The seven lamps of fire burning, or the seven colours of the rainbow, symbolize the covenant, the universal mediating principle. They unite the two notes symbolized by the two pebbles at the third level of the tetrad and represent that final semitone interval existing beyond the cosmic note 'ti', the point in time and space where the Same and the Other are fused into one, and where Christ, as is said, died. We are here on the plane of light, of course: the 'sanctuary that is above', dominion of the Holy Ghost.

The four and twenty elders with crowns of gold upon their heads together symbolize the Son, Jesus, whose name in Gematria has a value of 888. The four beasts 'full of eyes' before, behind and within (harmoniously composed within and without), depict the transcendental rhythm and motion of the whole musical phenomenon, the four base-notes.

The lion symbolizes the first, active force. The calf, the opposite passive coordinate, and the man neutral. When lion, calf and man live together in harmony, or resonate one to the other at optimum frequencies, then the whole triad subsequently becomes the centre of gravity of a new and entirely different manifestation of energy and form. That is, from the harmoniously balanced man, from within, is born the eagle, the transcendental ('flying') product of the union of the three.

> And when those beasts give glory and honour and thanks to him that sat on the throne, who liveth for ever and ever, the four and twenty elders fall down before him that sat on the throne, and worship him that liveth for ever and ever, and cast their crowns before the throne, saying . . .
>
> *Revelation* 4.9–10

This seems to imply that every time the three forces of 'intelligence' (active sensations, neutral emotions, passive or receptive impressions) are functioning at optimum frequencies, then the harmonious, transcendental 'signal' generated thereby (*in* time) strikes a real and lasting signature within the formation and sequence of the greater scale above (*beyond* time, in the realms of 'him that liveth for ever and ever'). Note that the four and twenty elders 'fall down': they submit, adopt a distinctively passive role. And then finally, at the cosmic note 'ti' and through the medium of *light*, they become as one with the Absolute. 888 – three complete and harmonious octaves of pure energy; or *pi*; the whole phenomenon; sealed, fulfilled, indivisible, individual.

> And there appeared a great wonder in heaven; a woman clothed with the sun, and the moon under her feet, and upon her head a crown of twelve stars.
>
> *Revelation* 12.1

Or, from a musical point of view, one complete and harmonious octave of cosmological energy and form. To be 'clothed' with the sun is to be 'resonating' in tune with the frequencies at which waves of light operate. In being a fully harmonious manifestation of energy and form, light itself must already contain the two semitone 'shocks' necessary to maintain a condition of optimum resonance. So we have one tetrad of sunlight:

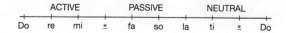

And, just to make sure this essentially musical message sinks in, John reminds us, as Christ had before, of the twelve further semitones inherent within any given concentration of resonance. The woman's crown refers precisely to these heaven-sent 'seals of the living God' (*Revelation* 7.2–4). The crown also suggests that the cosmological phenomenon symbolized by the woman is in fact composed of the degrees of resonance at which starlight operates; and the moon which, as we see, rests under her feet, indicates that the given phenomenon is also made up of the degrees of resonance characteristic of planetary formation. So the above tetrad, when harmoniously integrated with the twelve 'seals' or semitones – like so:

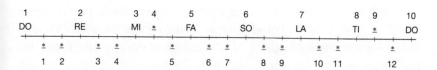

produces:

	STARS							SUN							PLANETS						
Do	re	mi	fa	so	la	ti	Do	re	mi	fa	so	la	ti	Do	re	mi	fa	so	la	ti	Do
1	2	3	4	5	6	7	8	9	10	11	12	13	14	15	16	17	18	19	20	21	22

Three interpenetrating octaves of cosmological energy and form.
The text continues:

> And she being with child cried, travailing in birth, and pained to be delivered.
>
> *Revelation* 12.2

The woman represents the passive force of the whole universal phenomenon. She is complete, fulfilled, 'resonating at optimum frequencies'; and in accordance with the laws of creation has acquired the power to generate, or 'give birth', to a new, transcendental phenomenon: the coming child.

> And there appeared another wonder in heaven; and behold a great red dragon, having seven heads and ten horns, and seven crowns upon his heads.
>
> *Revelation* 12.3

– a perfect description of the tetrad:

***	***	***		***	***	***	***		
1	2	3		4	5	6	7		
Do	re	mi	∗	fa	so	la	ti	∗	Do
1	2	3	4	5	6	7	8	9	10

> And his tail drew the third part of the stars of heaven, and did cast them to the earth: and the dragon stood before the woman which was ready to be delivered, for to devour the child as soon as it was born.
>
> *Revelation* 12.4

The dragon is the *active* force and is representative of the lower world of gross physical phenomena. Being red in colour, this tetrad depicts a subservient octave of cosmological energy and form, for the superior woman, remember, is clothed with the gold of the sun and has twelve stars set in a crown upon her head.

The subsequent outcome of this particular meeting of cosmic forces is that the child is 'born' and then 'caught up unto God and to His throne' (*Revelation* 12.5). Then follows a great war in heaven between the dragon and his angels and Michael and his angels, after which the defeated dragon is 'cast out into the earth' (*Revelation* 12.9).

The imagery invoked so far is lucid to say the least. As well as using the symbol of the woman to paint an overall cosmological and essentially musical picture of the universe, St John may also be suggesting that any natural-born woman 'travailing in birth' is under the direct influence of the sun, of the moon and planets, and of the stars, and having become a well-balanced passive force in the world of nature, so begins to resonate inwardly in such a manner that the signals of intelligence generated thereby actually strike real and lasting signatures 'out there' in the greater continuum. So the child (indeed all children, as we shall later see) is 'conceived' and then (this particular child at least) subsequently delivered upon the plane of light. Presumably the child in question will have been Christ, after his Ascension up into the greater scale above.

After this 'birth' the text describes how the woman apparently loses her 'seal', or her optimum degrees of resonance in the greater continuum. Significantly St John's account of the plight of the woman after the child has been delivered gives an exact musical description of the descent back to earth of an involving scale of resonance. The woman was given the wings of a great eagle, so that she might escape the wrath of the dragon and:

> . . . fly into the wilderness, into her place, where she is nourished for a time, and times, and half a time . . .
>
> *Revelation* 12.14

This particular phrase of St John's has confounded man for centuries, yet it depicts exactly the involutionary motion of a descending octave of resonance – so exactly, in fact, that one wonders how such a peculiarly haunting phrase could ever have escaped our attention for so long. A descending or involutionary octave begins resonating as a whole note with transcendental properties (denoted by the wings of the eagle). This note is complete (a time). It then involves through a series of lesser notes (and times), and ends with precisely half the number of vibrations – per second or whatever – that it had at the beginning of its involutionary movement (and half a time).

> And I stood upon the sand of the sea, and saw a beast rise up out of the sea, having seven heads and ten horns, and upon his horns ten crowns, and upon his heads the name of blasphemy.
>
> *Revelation* 13.1

– another perfect description of the tetrad.

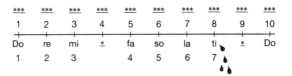

Well, almost:

> And I saw one of his heads as it were wounded to death; and his deadly wound was healed: and all the world wondered after the beast.
>
> And they worshipped the dragon which gave power unto the beast: and they worshipped the beast, saying, Who is like unto the beast? who is able to make war with him?
>
> *Revelation* 13.3–4

One can immediately notice a marked difference between the tetrad of this new manifestation – the sea beast – and that of the dragon. With the first phenomenon – the active force – it is the seven fundamental notes ('heads') themselves which are 'crowned'; whereas the second phenomenon – the sea beast – has crowns upon his ten 'horns'. The sea beast is representative of the corresponding *passive* force. One of its seven 'heads' or fundamental notes is 'wounded' (disharmonious), which means that only six of its notes are in a state of relative harmony. Subsequently, however, the concentration of vibrations represented by the 'dragon' tetrad (which is harmonious, at least within its own sphere of influence) generates degrees of resonance powerful enough to blend in with, and thus 'heal', the seventh head of the beast from the sea. So this phenomenon of the sea beast will henceforth be limited *in time* to within the boundaries of the dragon's sphere of influence – the dimension of planetary formation or three-dimensional space.

> And power was given unto him [the sea beast] to continue [blaspheming] forty and two months.
>
> *Revelation* 13.5

The sea beast is confined within an incomplete octave of time. Forty-two months is seven times six months. This suggests that seven times will the beast develop along an octave of time up to the sixth note, or stage of evolution – the metaphysical or cosmic note 'la', the level of being at which all earthly possibilities can be realized, the stage of the fool's enlightenment. For a 'beast' which cannot penetrate up to the degrees of resonance delineated by the seventh stage of the cosmic octave, the note 'la' represents its optimum level of power. Hence the time limit of forty-two months for, at the seventh stage, the cosmic note 'ti', forty-two-months' worth of time would merely evaporate. So this is the beast's true limitation. It cannot 'take time out', as it were, and 'rest'. To it, as it continues (actively) 'blaspheming', the sabbath is a meaningless concept. The beast cannot adopt the passive role in the universal drama, and so give birth to a new, transcendental manifestation of 'intelligent' resonance. In other words, it cannot penetrate up and onto the plane of light.

> And it was given unto him to make war with the saints, and to overcome them . . .
> And all that dwell upon the earth shall worship him, whose names are not written in the book of life of the Lamb slain from the foundation of the world.
>
> *Revelation* 13.7–8

To 'dwell upon the earth' is to have one's thoughts permanently bound down by simplistic earthly concepts. The phrase 'whose names are not written in the book of life of the Lamb' refers to those forms of intelligence which do not or cannot develop along the tetrad of individual time up into the degrees of resonance characteristic of the passive cosmic note 'ti'. They are limited to the power and the tone of the sixth note, 'la'. So, for a phenomenon such as the beast of Revelation, trapped as he is in the third dimension, at very best his endeavours can take him no further than the sixth stage of evolution.

Let us now return to the text. After the aforementioned forty-two months of 'blaspheming' on the part of the (sea) beast, another phenomenon is said to have occurred:

> And I beheld another beast coming up out of the earth; and he had two horns like a lamb, and he spake as a dragon.

And he exerciseth all the power of the first beast before him, and he causeth the earth and them which dwell therein to worship the first beast, whose deadly wound was healed.

Revelation 13.11–12

Remember the dragon itself is the first, active force in this cosmological and musical spectacular. Upon descending to the surface of the planet it then transfers some of its energies into the first beast, the beast from the sea. The sea beast, as we have said, is the passive manifestation of this cosmic fusion of forces. This passive manifestation has only six good 'heads' – the seventh being 'wounded' or out of tune, evidently having met with degrees of resonance greater and more powerful than its own. Eventually, however, the sea beast reaches what is, for it, an optimum level of resonance and, just as the dragon had done before, transfigurates some of its energies into the third phenomenon, the *neutral* manifestation described as the 'beast from the earth', looking as gentle as the proverbial lamb but possessing, in fact, all the internal attributes of the first two creatures, including the voice of the dragon.

As is evident so far, St John's unique portrayal of interpenetrating cosmic forces is nothing if not a detailed and wholly scientific treatise on the esoteric principles of musical notation. But if at this point we also bear in mind from whom it was that the author drew all his spiritual inspiration, then it will not be difficult for us to see that this remarkable text, as well as being an extremely artistic exposition on musical theory, is also an invaluable historic document which actually covers some of the key events of yesteryear with astonishing accuracy and breadth of vision. Remember that all the events described in the text transpire after an 'immaculate conception' or 'delivery' up onto the plane of light. This then, as has already been suggested, could well be a description of the universal effects, both upon the continuum 'without', and the planet earth 'within' of the 'birth' (self-realization) of Jesus Christ.

Thus the dragon represents man the animal, the natural force of the active, material world. The first beast – the passive manifestation rising out of the (Piscean) sea – represents none other than society itself, hence the seventh 'head', 'as it were wounded to death'. Indeed, had not Christ and his followers dealt a mortal blow to the all-too-decadent society of Jerusalem? Surely this is so. The incredible and totally unexpected psychological impact arising from the production of the Passion Play must have rocked the ill-constructed 'temples' of the scribes and Pharisees to their very foundations. And eventually, of course, as St John was evidently aware, the neutral product of a 'wounded' society would manifest itself through the formalized dogma of a hierarchical church. Then would follow the inevitable decline into dualistic perception (two horns) and self-deceit (clothed as a lamb but with the voice of a dragon). The text continues:

> And he doeth great wonders, so that he maketh fire come down from heaven on the earth in the sight of men.
> And deceiveth them that dwell on the earth by the means of those miracles which he had power to do in the sight of the beast; saying to them that dwell on the earth, that they should make an image to the beast, which had the wound by a sword, and did live . . .
> And he causeth all, both small and great, rich and poor, free and bond, to receive a mark in their right hand, or in their foreheads.
> And that no man might buy or sell, save he that had the mark, or the name of the beast, or the number of his name.
>
> *Revelation* 13.13–14, 16–17

In this way St John foreshadows the inevitable and eternal conspiracy between society and its neutral manifestation, the formalized church, which, as we read, has the power to perform so-called miracles 'in the sight of the beast', i.e. with its – society's – acquiescence. The 'great wonders' performed by this 'beast from the earth' would have been little more than subjectivized manipulations of the original hermetic ideas, many of the secrets of which will have been jealously hoarded away in the archives of early Christendom, and therefore far away from the curious eye of the genuine seeker. So with the aid of these wonders (squaring the circle, music, astronomical predictions of eclipses and so forth) the lamb beast easily confounds the people into believing that its degrees of resonance, *and* those of the sea beast's, are fully harmonious with all the forces of nature. And the true mark of the beast, as we see, is the mark of society itself – trade and profit – for 'no man might buy or sell, save he that had the mark'. But:

> Here is wisdom. Let him that hath understanding count the number of the beast: for it is the number of a man; and his number is Six hundred threescore and six.
>
> *Revelation* 13.18

666. The dragon of the air, the beast of the sea and the beast of the earth. Three interpenetrating tetrads of psychic energy and form with potential to generate 'signals' of intelligence only into the sphere of the planetary world; subservient always to the energy of the sun. 666 represents the three cosmic notes, 'la–la–la' of an evolutionary triple-octave; and neither the dragon, nor the first beast, nor the second – nor indeed all three combined – can ever develop consciously up to the seventh stage of evolution.

St John himself could not be clearer on this point: 'for it is the number of a man' – an ordinary man, Darwinian man. This, then, is the true beast of Revelation, a superficially powerful and hard-hitting species of animal blindly committed to the unenlightened doctrine of the survival of the fittest, one whose every move in the socialized world of the upwardly mobile is entirely automatic and self-motivated.

The Beatles encapsulated the true nature of the beast in one of their lesser-known songs:

> All through the day . . .
> 'I-me-mine, I-me-mine, I-me-mine . . .'
> All through the night . . .
> 'I-me-mine, I-me-mine, I-me-mine . . .'
>
> 'I-Me-Mine', *Let It Be*, 1969

Clearly no 'signals' generated by this kind of individual could ever enlighten anyone's mind. This is because such influences are purely subjective, anchored by habit, stale convention and negative human emotion to a narrow, simplistic and materialistic, three-dimensional world. And when the individuals responsible for generating such influences ultimately die, no matter how politically or financially powerful they may have been, their 'signals' inevitably die with them. They simply do not have the power to penetrate fully into the fourth dimension of time and beyond, into the minds and hearts of humankind, the metaphysical, the real world.

We have examined in this book only a fraction of the New Testament. There is, of course, much left unsaid, but perhaps it were better so, because the Gospel texts and St John's Book of Revelation have been designed principally to be experienced firsthand. New and deeper meanings tend to spring up from their timeless pages after every contemplative reading.

The Book of Revelation is possibly the most comprehensive hermetic treatise in existence. Notes from my own researches into St John's remarkable text would fill half a paperback or more, but at this stage I shall simply suggest that those interested in studying what I personally consider to be one of the most important pieces of literature ever written should take time out and read for themselves all twenty-two chapters – and more than once. It will become apparent to anyone who does so that the entire text is actually a detailed scientific commentary on the musical processes of transcendental evolution.

The whole of the New Testament, in fact, is composed along the same principles. In the beginning, the reader receives a first initiation, which is an introduction to the fundamental tenets of the Christian code. This is done through the oft-repeated guidelines of moral conduct contained within the *four* key Gospels: Matthew, Mark, Luke and John. The first three – the so-called 'synoptic' Gospels – have been identified by theologians as being factually similar. The fourth – that of John – is recognized as having, to quote C. H. Dodd, 'an individuality of its own', a different tone, as it were, from the first three. The Gospel of St John represents the fourth transcendental product arising from the harmonious combination of the synoptic triad. This would mark the end of the first stage of initiation into the noble mores of the hermetic order, forming the 'sound' base (or rock) upon which can be built St John's Eldorado, the New Jerusalem.

The second stage of initiation, beginning with the first book of Acts and ending with the message of Jude, is composed of *twenty-two* treatises. The last four of these – the three messages of John and the fourth by Jude – mark the end of the intermediary section of the whole work.

The next and last Book is Revelation, composed, not surprisingly, of *twenty-two* chapters.

Three major sections then: the *active* force of the first four Gospels; the reconciliatory messages of the twenty-two *neutral* intermediary treatises; and the *passive*, potentially transcendent complement to the complete series – the twenty-two chapters of Revelation.

CHAPTER ELEVEN

Zoroastrian refrains

I beheld a tree on which there were seven branches: one of gold, one of silver, one of copper, one of brass, one of lead, one of steel and one of blended iron.

Zand of Vahman Yasht, 3:20–1

Now that the principles at the root of the tetrad have been explained it will be possible to identify other significant examples of hermetic imagery left to us by the unknown authors of the earlier myths and legends of ancient Persia, the home of the three mysterious Magi of the Nativity story. The Indo-Iranian legends themselves are believed to have been gathered during the Vedic period between 1500 and 600 BC, although it was only toward the end of this era that they were finally committed to the written medium, no doubt playing an active role in the creation of the Zoroastrian and contemporary Indian Epic civilizations.

In pre-Zoroastrian Persia there were revered a number of so-called 'divine heroes'. The stories told of them frequently verge on the legendary rather than the mythical, but whether these heroes actually existed or not is a question that need not concern the passive and intuitive witness. One is seeking principally for keys to the secrets of universal harmony, for symbolized expressions of the age-old principle of 'acting out' a musical existence in time, and to this effect historical fact is of lesser consequence than the unchanging esoteric content of the symbolism itself. The important point to remember when speaking of such a remote period in history is that the names of these Vedic or Persian heroes, and the legends themselves, or myths or whatever, have succeeded in reaching twentieth-century man across three long and turbulent millennia of human history. One suspects that this is because they were designed to do so, having been purposefully introduced into the spheres of the human psyche by metaphysicians of the higher order, by 'musicians'.

The story of the divine hero Yima of Persian mythology, for example, clearly demonstrates the true nature and origin of Indo-Iranian cosmology. Yima is revered in Persia for his thousand-year rule over the earth, a rule characterized by peace and plenty, when evil demons and their evil deeds – famine, sickness, falsehood, death and so forth – had no place in the world. So well did the world prosper under Yima's rule that it had to be made larger, apparently on three successive occasions, so that at the end of his reign it was twice as large as when he began.

One is reminded here of St John's description of the plight of the woman in heaven who, upon fleeing to 'her place', 'was nourished for a time, and times, and half a time'. Yima's rule depicts just the opposite. Whereas the woman's fate in Revelation describes an involving scale of resonance, the record of Yima's achievements describes an evolving one, tripart in form, tenfold in sequence: a tetrad. And remember, a Pythagorean octave is the measure of the doubling of the rate of vibrations within any given scale. Yima, we are told, succeeded in doing just that – he doubled the size of the world, he 'squared' the tetrad. The tetrad, as we know, is fundamentally a tenfold concentration of resonance. When it achieves its optimum level of existence it acquires the power to unite with the combined constant forces of nature within, and also with the combined constant forces without. One exists 'above' (without), one exists 'below' (within), and one exists between the two. All are constant, all are the same, with a difference only in scale. We thus have in reality three tetrads in one, the harmonious combination of all of which can be described symbolically through the numerical formulation $10 \times 10 \times 10$, or a thousand years, the tetrad 'cubed'.

So Yima stood as the Persian personification of the true king, the ideal prototype for all rulers to emulate; and like all true adepts he conducted his planetary existence in strict accordance with the musical principle of transcendental evolution. Who exactly Yima was – if he existed at all – we shall possibly never know, although it is perhaps worth noting that the Vedic period itself encompasses the reign of Solomon, one of the most respected and successful kings in the whole of history. We are told that under Yima's rule the world prospered so well that, on three successive occasions, it had to be made larger. The same thing apparently happened in Solomon's day. The king of Israel was a great trader. Through his connections with neighbouring maritime Phoenicians he acquired a massive fleet of ships with which he effectively increased the size of the then-known world, extending his trade routes to the spice islands of Indonesia in the east, and to the western extremities of Europe and Africa (and also, if the sudden and mysterious upsurge in pyramid-building in Central and South America is to be explained with a modicum of rationale, across the Atlantic).

In Persia the goddess Ardui Sura Anahita is considered to be the endless source of all waters upon the earth. She is revered as being the wellspring of all fertility, purifier of the seed of all males, sanctifier of the womb of all females. An object of deep veneration in Persia, Anahita also became a popular deity in many other lands. To the Armenian she is the giver of life, mother of all wisdom and daughter of God, abiding always in her heavenly home, the source of the cosmic ocean. The imagery used to describe her is significant. She is held to be strong and bright, tall and beautiful, nobly born and pure, wearing always a golden crown with eight rays and a hundred stars upon her head, a golden mantle around her body and a golden necklace around her neck.

This description bears a striking resemblance to the image of the woman in heaven in Revelation. The eight rays of the crown is a symbol of the sun, of the fundamental notes of an octave of light, and the hundred stars denote that this particular tetrad, in being a tenfold concentration of resonance operating at optimum frequencies, has already 'given birth' to a 'child' – i.e. is a 'squared' phenomenon. Anahita is the universal passive force, whose day is the sabbath and whose spheres of influence reach up from the lowest degrees of resonance of planetary formations, to the highest degrees characteristic of the metaphysical or cosmic note 'ti' – the point where our separate, materially bound perceptions of space and time effectively unite, through light, into a single, individual, whole conception.

Another interesting power-possessor of the Persian cosmos is a creature known as the Druj (meaning 'lie' or 'deceit'), a term used to describe a fiend or demon. The most notorious of these demons is Azhi Dahaka, son of the great Evil Spirit, an embodiment of the malevolent force described as the 'destructive desire'. Dahaka is depicted as being possessed of three heads, six eyes and three jaws, with a body that is so full of lizards, scorpions and other gruesome life forms that, were he to be cut open, the world would be swamped by them. On one occasion this infamous demon apparently offered in sacrifice to the goddess Anahita one hundred horses, one thousand oxen and ten thousand lambs, praying that he might be permitted the gratification of his one desire – the extermination of all life on earth. The offer was, of course, made in vain.

Once again we see a remarkable likeness between the imagery used to describe this Persian demon, Dahaka, and that of another infamous demon – the 'beast' of Christian inspiration. Dahaka has only six eyes (notes). He is incomplete, universally disharmonious, and even if he were to 'square' his possibilities (horses, oxen, lambs), he would still be unable to penetrate up into the degrees of resonance at which Anahita exists and operates. Dahaka is the Zoroastrian representative of the negative aspect of the universal active force, limited by his powers of vision (the eyes), to the sixth note, the cosmic note 'la'.

Zoroastrians believe that the present process of world history lasts for twelve thousand years, and that we are now living in the final of four distinct three-thousand-year periods. During this final world age they expect three saviours to appear at one-thousand-year intervals. The first was expected one thousand years after their prophet and, as he himself is thought to have lived around 600 BC, this suggests that the first two saviours should have made their presences felt by now.

The first 'millennium' of the final world age was further subdivided into four unequal subordinate periods, each being symbolized by a metal. According to contemporary Zoroastrian belief, the age of gold represents the time of Zoroaster himself, when the Good Religion was first revealed to the prophet. Silver denotes the age when the prophet's royal patron adopted the formalized religion; steel for the Sassanian period, beginning around AD 220, and iron for the present time, when the Good Religion is expected to rapidly decline. Recognizing neither Christianity nor Islam, Zoroastrians consider the prophecies of the second and third comings as having yet to be fulfilled, and have accordingly made theoretical amendments to the original exposition of their founder by suggesting that between the ages of steel and iron there are three further periods of brass, copper and lead. The first 'millennium' of this final world age has thus been inexplicably extended indefinitely and presently occupies over two and a half times its original expected duration, which presumably accounts for the nonappearance of their first saviour as he is still not due.

Obviously this somewhat confusing attempt to manipulate time misses the true significance of Zoroaster's all-wise message. Each of these metallic ages is in fact a symbol of pure hermetic design, and they represent the four fundamental base-notes of an involving triple-octave of resonance. Zoroaster himself sounded the first age, the first note, 'Do', harmonious within, harmonious without and – as we today can intuit – transcendental in the extreme. The thousand-year period between the appearance of Zoroaster and the next base-note, the arising of the next fully realized initiate or saviour, is not only a literal measure of time, but also a symbolized expression of an involving tetrad of time. This first 'thousand-year' period need not, therefore, be one thousand years. It could be ten, it could be fifty, or five hundred, or seven thousand . . . weeks, years or even seconds. From a true hermetic perspective ordinary temporal exactitude is not so important. What Zoroaster is really saying is simply that the tenfold period of transition between the age of gold and the age of iron is in reality a whole, harmonious, law-conformable unit.

Of the first saviour it is prophesied that he will be the 'developer of righteousness' and will bear the name Aushedar. When Aushedar reaches the age of thirty, strange and wonderful things will happen. The sun will stand still for ten days at the noonday position, where it had apparently stood before the first earthly attack of the demon Ahriman. It is further stated that the saviour will confer with the archangels and bring with him the revelation first brought by Zoroaster. For three years thereafter man will live more harmoniously with the forces of nature and a certain part of malevolent creation – the 'wolf' species – will disappear.

As it was with Zoroaster, Aushedar's coming promised to be yet another 'immaculate conception'. The tetrad itself is represented by the symbol of the sun, an harmonious octave of light which, at the end of the saviour's third decade on earth will stand still in the sky for ten days at the noonday position. So for ten days, in the twelve-o'clock position, the eight rays of the sun shine constantly. Small wonder perhaps for, as we can see, we have here yet another perfect hermetic description of the innermost composition of the major Pythagorean octave. It is particularly significant that the first saviour is expected to bring harmony to the world for just three years. This means that, from the time of his arising to the moment when the part of evil creation designated by the 'wolf' species finally disappears, is a period of exactly thirty-three years – precisely the purported age at which the initiate Jesus Christ died.

To the orthodox Zoroastrian this more than tentative suggestion that Jesus could have been the first saviour and regenerator of the Good Religion (Christianity is certainly that) would no doubt be considered as heresy. Perhaps so. One can but speculate. The active, 'fire-worshipping' aspect of Zoroastrianism with its emphasis on 'doing' is, it must be admitted, fundamentally different from the passive, contemplative approach encoded within the principle of love of the Christian faith. But if one accepts that the common denominator of both of these creeds is in reality the musical principle of transcendental evolution, then this fact alone unites these two metaphysical phenomena, through the medium of time, into a temporal, spatial and 'intelligent' whole, with an active principle (Zoroastrianism), a passive principle (Christianity) and a neutral principle (the thousand-year, or tetradic, time-span). Incidentally the description of Aushedar's sun standing still for ten days at the noonday position also fits remarkably well into the pattern of future events if we visualize Christ as being representative of the fundamental ten-day period, and his disciples as being symbolized by the twelve subordinate hours of the clock.

*

Zoroaster, like Christ and/or the first saviour, began his earthly ministry after his thirtieth year. These three decades symbolize the optimum level of development of three evolutionary tetrads of 'intelligent' resonance: sensational, emotional and perceptual. In Zoroaster's case this marked the time when he transcended the lower scale of his origin, and then proceeded, through a series of eight visions, to develop along a greater octave of resonance existing beyond time (in heaven), where he subsequently entered into the presence of the famous seven beings, the so-called Amesha Spentas or Bounteous Immortals, sons and daughters of God. All seven are depicted as sitting on golden thrones beside the Creator in a place called the House of Song.

The first of the seven beings is Vohu Manah, or Good Mind. Good Mind sits at the right hand of God, acting almost as adviser, and denotes the seventh note, 'ti'. Good Mind is the transcendental product of the passive mind and represents the union of the Same and the Other, or of consciousness and light. According to Zoroaster, Good Mind is the entity who keeps a daily record of man's thoughts and deeds. This is the 'book of life' of the Christian Lamb, the plane of light. At death the soul is greeted by Good Mind and led by him to the highest heaven (provided, one assumes, that the soul has developed an inner resonance powerful enough to withstand the shock of death).

The second Bounteous Immortal is Asha, or Truth, and denotes the cosmic note 'la'. Asha is purportedly the most beautiful of the Immortals and bears the particular distinction of being 'the opposite of the lie'. The word 'lie' in Persian (druj), as we have noted, is also used to describe a demon or beast. So Asha is the truth and the Druj is its opposite. In point of fact, this idea was also reflected in later Christian thought. The two phrases in St John's Book of Revelation, 'the Son of Man' and 'the image of the beast' each have a value in Gematria of 2260. These two principles are meant to represent the opposite coordinates of one and the same phenomenon: the universal active force. The Son of Man (Asha, the truth) is the positive aspect; and the beast himself (Druj, the lie) is the negative aspect. Upon entering the degrees of resonance operating at the cosmic note 'la', the positive aspect generates upward to the note 'ti'. The negative aspect naturally degenerates downward to the note 'so' and beyond. So Asha represents that certain and attainable degree of psychic or intelligent resonance within which is encoded the secret of death, of dying, i.e. of transmuting up into the realms of the Good Mind, into the degrees of resonance characteristic of the passive cosmic note 'ti'.

Denoting the degrees of resonance generated at the cosmic note 'so' is an entity called Kshathra Vairya, or the Desired Kingdom. This symbol is the most abstract of the Immortals. Kshathra Vairya is said to be the protector of metals and is associated with a certain stream of molten metals that will test men and women at the end of the world. The stream is taken to represent the final defeat of evil, a kind of psychic purification process which would 'level the earth and sweep over all men'. The molten condition of the metals is interesting in that it describes the unification of several separate elements into a single new state, liquid – a new phenomenon which, quite unlike the solids from which it was formed, flows freely.

The notes, 'fa', 'mi' and 're' are represented by the entities Armaiti (Devotion), Armeretat (Immortality) and Haurvatat (Integrity); and whereas the first three – Good Mind, Truth and the Desired Kingdom – are depicted as male deities, Devotion, Immortality and Integrity are said to be female. Armaiti (Devotion) is the daughter of the Creator and sits at His left hand. Her name means literally 'fit-mindedness'. She thus represents the fundamental thinking processes of the evolving entity, the cosmic note 'fa'. Immortality and Integrity are always mentioned together in Zoroastrian texts. Usually associated with water, Immortality is said to be the counterbalance to the human condition of thirst; and Integrity, in being associated with the world of vegetation, is considered to be the counterbalance to the condition of hunger. First is Immortality. This is the cosmic note 'mi', suitably allied to the symbol of water which, as we know, is matter in molecular state, the principal fuel, as it were, of all emotional processes. Integrity is the note 're'. From its close association with the cellular world of vegetation, we may assume that this represents the physical body itself, our sensations.

The final Immortal (or rather, from the point of view of man's potential evolution, the first) is Sraosha, or Obedience, one of the most popular figures in ancient Persian culture. Sraosha is said to be the conveyor of prayers to heaven, the 'holy ritual chief' who was the first to chant the *Gathas* (hymns) of the prophet (evidently a direct reference to the first note 'Do' of an ascending octave of resonance). The description of Sraosha's house is worth noting. It is said to rest on the highest peak of Mount Harait, to be built upon a thousand pillars, self-lit within and lit by stars without. In other words: perfect harmony, $10 \times 10 \times 10$ – the tetrad 'cubed'. We hear also that Sraosha is drawn from his house in his chariot pulled by four beautiful white horses with swift golden feet; and that it is he who greets and watches over the soul at death. He would do, of course, for Sraosha and the Creator are one and the same phenomenon, but with a difference only in scale.

The Creator Himself – the ultimate note, 'Do', of the cosmic octave – is called Ahura Mazda (meaning 'Wise Lord'), but his essential characteristic is defined, not surprisingly, by an eighth Immortal, Spenta Mainyu (Bounteous or Creative Spirit). According to the traditions of the Magi this characteristic belongs to God alone, whereas the other seven beings are all facets of God in which man, through the right kind of effort, can share.

Only fragments of Zoroaster's twenty-one treatises have reached us today, but even from the little that has filtered down one can still find clear traces of hermetic lore. Yasht (hymn) fourteen, for example, the Zoroastrian text dedicated to the ancient Persian god of victory, Verethragna, has an altogether familiar ring to it. Contemporary thought has tended toward the idea that this particular god is simply an abstraction, a personification of an idea. This rather woolly exegesis is based on the belief that Verethragna is principally an expression of the aggressive, irresistible force of victory – which indeed he is. But he is also much more. The symbolism used to describe him, in fact, is yet another perfect description of an evolutionary tetrad. Verethragna is said to have ten incarnations or forms, each form representing one of the dynamic forces invoked by his spirit. The first incarnation is that of a strong wind; the second takes the form of a bull with golden horns and yellow ears; the third, that of a white horse bridled with gold; the fourth, a heavily laden camel stamping forward; the fifth, a sharp-toothed male boar; the sixth, that of a youth at the ideal age (in Persian thought) of fifteen; the seventh, the form of a swift bird –

possibly a raven; the eighth, a wild ram; the ninth, that of a fighting buck; and finally the tenth, described as a man holding a sword with a golden blade.

WIND	BULL	HORSE	CAMEL	BOAR	YOUTH	RAVEN	RAM	BUCK	MAN
Do	re	mi	±	fa	so	la	ti	±	Do

The symbol of the primordial wind fits well enough. The bull and the horse at the notes 're' and 'mi' both have gold about them. They are full notes, 'hermetically sealed' and therefore harmonious within and without. The first semitone position is occupied by the image of the burden-bearing camel, suitably depicted as stamping forward, that is, in motion; he is going somewhere and has work to do, energy to transmit. The next four symbols – boar, youth, raven and ram – are somewhat obscurely chosen. In Persia the two incarnations of the raven and the boar were particularly popular. The Magi tended to view the raven's feathers with awe, and of Verethragna's incarnation as the boar it is ominously written in another Zoroastrian hymn:

. . . he cuts to pieces everything at once, mingling together on the ground the bones, the hair, the brains and the blood of men false to the contract . . .

Yasht 10:70–2

Superimposed over the cosmic octave described in Revelation, the 'sharp-toothed boar' would occupy the station of the first eight of the twenty-four 'elders':

MAN

RAM   BUCK

BOAR   YOUTH   RAVEN

WIND   BULL   HORSE   CAMEL

No man 'false to the contract' can ever pass the boar, the cosmic note 'fa'. The implication is that any disharmonious degrees of psychic resonance encountering the constant forces operating at such a level of existence would simply disintegrate, or be torn to pieces. The three notes (inner octaves) and one semitone below must be harmoniously interrelated one to the other before further evolution is possible. So the reference in the text of Yasht ten, to bone, hair, brains and blood mingling together on the ground is directly related to the four fundamental base-notes of an evolving tetrad of 'intelligent' resonance. Hair, which is dead from the root upward, denotes the wind, the force of the spirit; bones symbolize the body and its sensations; blood stands for the heart, for emotions; and brains for the mind, for perceptions. The transcendental product of this harmonious inner triad – the boar itself – then has the possibility to develop uniformly up to the cosmic note 'ti'. Then comes the final semitone. Like the first semitone this is depicted by the symbol of an animal in motion, the fighting buck. The ultimate symbol of the man with the golden sword speaks well enough; it is simply spiritual fulfilment, inner harmony and transcendental power – the greatest 'victory' man can ever achieve.

An Eastern parallel to Verethragna is the legend of the ten avatars or incarnations of Vishnu. The first three incarnations have reference to a great Deluge such as is referred to in the scriptures of most religions. The Hindu account of the Flood states that Manu (of the ten great sages) received orders from Brahma to construct a great ship and take on board seven holy men and the seeds of all living beings. When the flood came, Vishnu appeared in the form of the first avatar, Matsya, a great fish which came and towed Manu's ship to a high peak, where it rested until the waters had subsided. Vishnu's next incarnation followed soon afterward in the form of Kurma, a tortoise which during the flood recovered many valuable articles from the bottom of the sea. The third avatar, obviously of Vedic origin, was the *boar*, Varaha, who fought with the demon Hiranyaksa and raised the earth, which had been cast into a great gulf by his foe. The fourth descent was in the form of Nara-Sinha, the man-lion who came to earth to deal with the demon king Hiranya after he had tried to slay his own son who had displeased him by worshipping Vishnu. Vamana, Vishnu's fifth incarnation, was a dwarf who ordered a sacrilegious king named Bali to give him as much territory as he could stride over in three paces. When King Bali unwittingly complied with the request the dwarf suddenly assumed enormous proportions and, traversing heaven and earth with his first two steps, duly placed the third step firmly on the king's head and crushed him into oblivion.

The sixth descent took the form of the warrior Parasu Rama, who travelled the earth slaying irreverent Kshatriyas (the warrior caste) who had taken to ill-treating Brahmins. The seventh, one of Vishnu's most popular incarnations, was Rama, legendary slayer of countless demons, who ruled his people with infinite wisdom and justice. Vishnu descended for the eighth time in the form of Krishna, the warrior Arjuna's spiritual and moral guide in the great battle of Kurashestra described in the *Bhagavad-Gita*. The Buddha is regarded as the ninth incarnation. Vishnu is said (by traditionalist Hindus) to have assumed the Buddha's form to deceive mankind into neglecting the ritual worship of the gods and hasten the world's ruin. The tenth avatar is yet to come and will appear at the end of the present age, the Kali Yuga, in the form of the Kalkin, punisher of the wicked. It is said that the Kalkin will ultimately be revealed in the sky, riding a white steed, with a *flaming sword* in his hand.

Further exact parallels to the Zoroastrian, Vedic and other ancient testaments can be recognized in many other traditions. In fact, knowledge of the hermetic code itself appears to have spread across the entire planet at a very early stage in our recorded history. As we might expect, one of the most fundamental symbols of the code – the septenary principle – was first identified in the night sky above the Nile Delta, observed by Egyptian astronomers as the seven large stars of the Great Bear, or Plough. Otherwise known as the Mother of Time, the Great Bear was simply a celestial expression of the universal passive force, equivalent to the goddess Anahita mentioned earlier in this chapter, the archetypal 'woman in heaven', the cosmic note 'ti'. The Egyptians further divided the whole of the night sky into seven separate sections and there are significant references in Egyptian texts to the 'seven souls' of the dead pharaoh.

The Hindus also looked upon the Great Bear as being the heavenly abode of the Septarishi, an embodiment of the seven primitive Rishis (or properties) applicable to the whole of nature – hence their description of the seven peninsulas, the seven islands, the seven rivers, seas and mountains of India.

The Mosaic division of the week into seven days is a temporal expression of the same principle. Thus, if we take the main units of time and set them down in our usual way, we see a familiar overall picture:

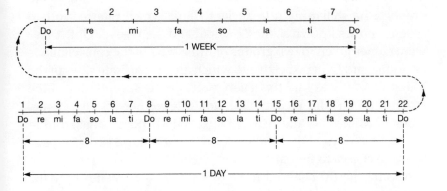

An hour is traditionally regarded as being the *time* taken to journey, through *space*, a distance of three miles. Interestingly enough, the English mile itself is also hermetically composed. It comprises eight furlongs, each of which consists of ten chains, each chain being a measure of exactly twenty-two yards. Moreover, a · *square* mile encompasses precisely 640 acres.

Much further afield – an ocean apart, in fact – the American Zuni Indians built virtually all of their social and religious institutions upon the septenary principle. All their settlements were invariably constructed in clusters of six dwellings around a seventh; and their priestly class consisted of six Priests of the House, all of whom were answerable to a seventh, a (passive) woman known as the Priestess Mother. Traditionally Zuni priests would receive from their people an annual gift of corn of seven colours, each colour sacred to the particular god personified by the given priest, each in turn representing one of the seven great regions of their homeland. This principle of 'coloured corn' found similar expression in the ancient traditions of the Eskimo, who distinguishes, according to colour, texture and so on, seven different kinds of snow.

The creation myth of the Mayan civilization, arguably one of the oldest known cultures of Central America, refers to a pantheon of seven solar deities, or regents, who formed a council and between them generated the 'Word', i.e. the creative act. According to the *Popul Vuh*, the Mayan bible, or Book of Advice, these seven gods presided over a universe consisting of three quadrilaterals placed on top of the other: the first represented the sky, the second the earth, and the third the underworld.

Long before the Mayan civilization came into being, there originated a stellar myth in ancient China which referred to two cosmic entities known as the Cowherd and the Weaver Girl. These were names given to two groups of three stars in the constellations of Aquila and Lyra respectively, which are on opposite sides of the Milky Way. It was said that every year, on the seventh day of the seventh moon, the Weaver Girl would leave her celestial home, cross the Milky Way and go to her husband. (In point of fact, during the first ten days of the seventh lunar month, these two groups of stars are closest to the earth.)

Another myth, believed to be of Celtic origin, relates how the sorceress Cessair (possibly a derivation of the Greek goddess, Circe) perished with the whole of her race. Subsequently Partholon, a prince from Greece, landed in Ireland with twenty-four couples. In the beginning Ireland was a glass-like plain broken by three lakes and watered by nine rivers, but it was later modified by Partholon and thenceforward existed as four plains with seven new lakes.

Again in Celtic mythology, the centre of spiritual insight was Avalon, the fabled Isle of Appletrees, which corresponded to the old Druidic sanctuary called the Isle of Sein, otherwise known as the Isle of Seven Sleeps. Like the ancient Egyptians, the Druids themselves believed in the seven souls of the departed.

Back nearer the original source, the ancient Persians lit seven fires, said to have burned continuously in front of the altars of Mithra. The Arabians had their seven 'Fanes' (shrines); the Kabbalistic 'tree of life' is referred to in the *Zohar* as the Sephiroth of the Seven Splendours; and the Chaldeans saw the world as comprising seven spheres, occupied in turn by the seven Great Spirits. The four-thousand-year-old Sumerian epic known as the Poem of Creation was inscribed on seven tablets and speaks of the nature of the two cosmic deities, Anshar and Kishar, as representing, respectively, the things above, of the sky (An) and the things below, of the Earth (Ki). Equally as old are certain texts of early Semitic mythology found at Ras Shamra, which refer to the various victories in battle won by Baal's sister Anat (yet another version of the Mother of Time), who slew her brother's worst foes, Tannin, the dragon-prince of the sea, and Loran, the tortuous serpent, the beast with seven heads.

Many deities of Greek mythology also held the number seven in the highest esteem, as did those of the Roman pantheon. Thus the god Mars was said to have had seven attendants; Atlas had his seven daughters (the Pleiades); Apollo ruled over his seven planets and played hymns to the 'seven-rayed' on a seven-stringed harp; and the name Zeus, beginning with the Greek letter 'Z' – which is a double seven – is simply a reflection of yet another great god, the Jehovah of the seven letters.

In current folklore, every seventh wave is something special, described, often ominously, as being the wave to watch out for – the idea being, perhaps, that one should remember the seventh (the sabbath) or risk drowning in a veritable ocean of time.

On the brighter side, the value of remembering the significance of the sabbath is neatly summed up in a well-known piece of nursery verse:

> One, two, three, four, five, six, seven,
> All good children go to heaven.

– and again:

> One for sorrow, two for joy,
> Three for a girl and four for a boy,
> Five for silver, six for gold,
> Seven for a secret never to be told . . .

In triple form, the septenary principle can again be traced directly back to ancient Egypt, whose principal god Osiris had his body dissected into seven and twice seven separate parts. Zoroaster later adopted the same format when composing his twenty-one *Nasks*, which in turn were both forerunner and probable inspiration for St John's twenty-two chapters of the Book of Revelation. I have already mentioned the ten avatars or incarnations of Vishnu, but in fact in another Hindu myth described in the *Purana* texts, he is described as having reincarnated twenty-one times, with the twenty-second incarnation yet to come. This *pi* formula has of course persisted right up to the present day and can still be recognized in certain well-known modern traditions, such as the Western twenty-first birthday celebrations at which those entering the final stage of adulthood are ceremonially given the key to the door. The same principle lies behind the twenty-one gun salute sounded for the departed souls of warriors, and the original twenty-one disciplines of the Greek-inspired Olympic Games.

The esoteric number twelve, which, as we now know, is also essentially a symbol of the octave (i.e. the twelve intermediate tones), has also appeared and reappeared over the ages, many times and in many guises. Remember the Persian Magi, who prophesied that the second coming would cause the sun to stand still for ten days at the twelve-o'clock position. This 'zodiacal' tradition, which in fact existed long before the time of the Chaldean astrologers, continued through Christianity (the twelve disciples), Islam (the Shiite 'Twelvers'), and even Western folklore (the Arthurian legend of the Knights of the Round Table).

According to one early Chinese myth of creation, the world originally had ten suns and twelve moons, which in turn corresponds with the Chinese calendar system based on a combination of ten 'trunks' and twelve 'branches'. One is here reminded of another symbolic 'tree', the Sephiroth of the Kabbalah, which is also based on a similar combination of ten and ten-plus-twelve, namely, the ten 'primordial numbers' and the twenty-two letters of the Hebraic alphabet.

As our 'musical' journey through time progresses further, we shall see that *all* the key symbolic numbers of the hermetic code, from the trinity (three) right through to the square of the constant (sixty-four), have in fact remained prominent features of most if not all of man's higher intellectual disciplines, be they religious, philosophical or, indeed, scientific.

Thus the seal of the Hermetic Order did not, as many Christians believe, disappear with the Grail. Clearly it could never vanish altogether because, as we have seen, the many streams of hermetic influence had permeated man's time and space to such an overall extent that practically every great culture of the ancient world had embraced one or other of the code's musical formulae. It was acknowledged in an earlier chapter that at the beginning of the Christian era the science of Revelation had become an invisible, 'forbidden art', lost to all but the few. The mysterious Son of Man composed his own unique variation on the original theme with stunning artistry, but possibly he was able to do so only because the basic tenet of universal harmony was by this time an integral and irremovable part of man's race-memory, constantly influencing the development of human consciousness in many different and subtle ways. Indeed, so it has endured to the present day, as the remaining chapters of this book are intended to show.

CHAPTER TWELVE

The march of Islam

Now I am called the shepherd of the desert gazelles,
Now a Christian monk,
Now a Zoroastrian.
The Beloved is Three, yet One.
Just as the three are in reality one.

'Doctor Maximus' (Ibn El-Arabi)

For several hundred years AD the newest manifestion of the oldest
of creeds flourished. Now it was called Christianity. From that
original, perfect demonstration of living art acted out in time by the
initiate Jesus, emanated endless streams of real metaphysical light.
A whole new consciousness was born. Love, not simply the Law,
was to become the new way for millions.

Post-Christian society received many a wise message from this
new fellowship: 'Except ye . . . become as little children,' (passive,
receptive) 'ye shall not enter into the kingdom of heaven.',
'. . . count the number of the beast: for it is the number of a man'
(the lesser 'man', the Darwinian animal). The 'signals' were
everywhere: artistically created, objectively transmitted, musically
coded. The Gospels, the Passion narrative, the Book of Revelation
and the image of the New Jerusalem – as we have seen, all of these
writings are hermetic texts, 'religiously' set out strictly according to
the immaculate precepts of the first Egyptian founder of magic.

Through the ministries of individuals directly in tune with these
precepts – such as the first-century magus Apollonius of Tyana –

that 'other' form of Christianity known as Gnosticism persisted and flowed deep underground, remaining characteristically obscured from the formalized social hierarchy. A highly revered and saintly man, to whom many supernatural powers were attributed, Apollonius, a disciple of Pythagoras, led an active ministry which reputedly spanned almost a century. The Palestinian Essenes also, the secret order of Kabbalistic Jews of which John the Baptist is said to have been a one-time associate, must also have left their indelible marks, the Kabbalah itself being perhaps the greatest of them. And, from the overall musical format of the Greek version of the New Testament, we can assume that the key tenets of Pythagorean revelation, inherited, in part, from the Persian sage Zoroaster, were an integral part of the secret sciences being taught in the esoteric schools of the day. Palestine would at this time have been a seething mass of itinerant humanity, influenced from one direction by Egypt itself, from another by the Babylonian centres of culture and learning, and yet again by the Persian, the Greek and the Judaic streams of thought. But it was the 'immaculately conceived' creed known as Christianity which was to rise up out of this cultural mêlée and become the chief inspiration behind the evolutionary consciousness of the Western mind, the 'guiding light'.

. Inevitably, before too many centuries have passed, the great mediator Time intervenes once again and the whole story repeats itself in modified form. First we had the initial, vital spark, the creative or 'divine' Revelation. Gradually, naturally, the inner fire begins to die down. The original initiates pass over and others dutifully follow; but some merely imitate, turn inwardly and form a caste which begins once more to conceal and withhold. A hierarchy is formed, ritual grows cold, becomes repetitive, devoid of meaning, and dogma begins to cloud the intuitive mind. In short, the psychological milieu decreases in quality of resonance and a whole new 'beast', a whole new suffocating structure is unconsciously constructed upon the ever-shifting foundations of that illusory entity, society.

A group of followers known as the Nestorian Christians eventually became so disillusioned with the self-motivated elements of the new hierarchy that they finally broke away from the Orthodox Church of Byzantium. By the fifth century they were already spreading their unexpurgated knowledge rapidly through Asia

Minor. Their translations of early Greek manuscripts into their own tongue, Syriac, were duly received and assimilated by many who might otherwise have been passed over as being unworthy of 'salvation' – including, of course, the newly arisen clusters of Arab communities. In this way the scene was set for the stupendous onslaught of the Prophet Mohammed, the enigmatic warrior/ revolutionary who, in only a few short years, created the initial impetus for the evolutionary phenomenon which was to thunder across fourteen centuries of time in the metaphysical form of Islam, from Medina to Toledo and Granada, from Mecca to Bokhara and Lahore.

To anyone who is unaccustomed to the emotional fervour of the Islamic religion, the phenomenon itself might appear to be some-what overzealous. In fact, were the orthodox Christian, whose only experience of ritual worship has been gained amid the chill and often empty churches of Christendom, to venture inside one of Islam's many magnificent mosques, he might understandably find such an experience a little disquieting, particularly so if the place of worship happens to be also the tomb of a great imam. In such places one will witness displays of human passion and emotion of an intensity equalled by no other religion in the world. Mohammed calls the faithful to prayer before sunrise, just after noon, again in the late afternoon, again in the early evening and, the last call, immediately after sundown.

One man calls and even now, after fourteen centuries, millions come. Full name: Abulqasim Mohammed Ibn (1) Abdullah Ibn (2) Al-Muttalib Ibn (3) Hashim – 'thrice-great' – the man to whom a staggering one-seventh of the world's population owes its entire spiritual inspiration. Logically of course, this kind of otherwordly influences over the lives of so many is, we shall have to admit, practically inexplicable. Over the years literally thousands of books have been written about the phenomenon and it would be true to say that there are almost as many theories about the Prophet himself as there are biographers. As the reader might expect, to these we must now add another, the definitive theory – a final 'note', as it were – based on the assumption that Islam's code was yet another masterly cover version of the oldest song on earth.

*

The Muslim believes his Prophet to have been a modest, unlettered man, who became a vehicle, or 'transmitter', through which the Archangel Gabriel recited God's words. The Koran, Islam's Last Testament, was thus born. It is regarded as the record of those formal utterances which Mohammed and his followers accepted as divinely inspired. In outward form the Koran is a book of some three hundred pages, divided into 114 chapters called suras. These suras are arranged roughly in order of length, except for the short prayer which constitutes sura I. Sura II has 286 verses, sura III two hundred and so on down to the final suras comprising just three to five short verses. As the later, so-called Medinian suras are generally the longer ones, the order in which they appear is not chronological. The earlier Meccan verses, full as they are of striking poetic images and short, lyrical phrases, contrast greatly with the long, drawn out laws and exhortations characteristic of the later style, a difference which leads the more sceptical observer to conclude that the Archangel Gabriel's – and therefore God's – literary abilities leave much to be desired. This question of literary merit, however, should not be judged solely on a priori grounds, but in relation to the genius of the most archaic of all living Semitic languages, Arabic. As the Arabic scholar Sir Hamilton Gibb has pointed out, no man in fifteen hundred years has ever played on that deep-toned instrument with such power, such boldness and such range of emotional effect as Mohammed did.

So the Koran, whether it matches up to today's literary standards or not, is no ordinary book. Through it, the 'unlettered' Prophet Mohammed has succeeded in transmitting signals of intelligence which, over the centuries, have entered and blended harmoniously with the psychological presences of countless millions the world over. It was designed to have just this effect, of course, for, as we shall see, like all other major bodies of ancient law, the Koran is an essentially 'musical' treatise, founded purely and simply upon the unerring principles of hermetica.

Let us now examine the book itself. Remember that the suras, which have been faithfully preserved in the form in which they were originally conceived, are intended for recitation, for reading out loud; and, of all the suras, there can be none which has been repeated more often in space and time than the opening one, the Sūrat-ol-Fateha. Here is a translation:

In the Name of God, the Compassionate, the Merciful

Praise be to God, Lord of the worlds!
The compassionate, the merciful!
King on the day of reckoning!
Thee *only* do we worship, and to Thee do we cry for help
Guide Thou us on the straight path,
The path of those to whom Thou has been gracious; – with
    whom Thou art not angry, and who go not astray.

Sura I, 1–7

The *straight* path. Significantly the Sūrat-ol-Fateha, placed first in the Koran because of the importance it holds in Islamic prayer, is made up of seven verses, called the 'seven repetitions'. The invocation 'In the Name of God, the Compassionate, the Merciful' is here numbered as a separate verse, but in the other suras it is not. The rest of sura I therefore consists of six subordinate or subsidiary verses.

The observance of ritual prayers (*salāh*) is repeatedly emphasized as one of the essential religious duties. Although neither the set times of prayer nor the ceremonies are precisely stated in the Koran, most islamic scholars agree that they were well-established before Mohammed's death. Each consists of a certain number of bowings (*rak'ah*), the bowing itself comprising seven movements with their prescribed recitations:

1 Recitation of the phrase 'Allāhu akbar!' – 'God is Most Great', with the hands open on each side of the face
2 Recitation of the seven verses of the Sūrat-ol-Fateha and another or other passages while standing upright
3 Bowing from the hips
4 Straightening up
5 Gliding to the knees
6 Sitting back on the haunches
7 A final prostration

Mohammed's real intention thus becomes clear and we see that his followers, in their loyal observance of these ritual prayers, have in reality been living, or acting out, harmonious octaves of thought and deed in space and time. That such an octave *is* harmonious is attested by the fact that the sequence of bowings, which begins with the affirmative or active assertion: 'God is Most Great', ends, after a series of seven movements, in the submissive or passive act of silent prostration.

The Koran also mentions the noon prayer on Friday, the principal congregational prayer of the week, and advises the suspension of work during that day – thus indicating that Mohammed was also aware of the objective value in the culmination of a working week with a seventh, passive day. Interestingly enough the very name, Islam, adopted by Mohammed as the distinctive name of his faith, means 'submitting' (oneself to God) and is precisely that kind of psychological posture to which Christ alluded when advising his followers to 'turn the other cheek', to voluntarily adopt a passive role in the cosmic scheme of things.

The famous *shahāda* or profession of faith, 'lā ilāha illa'llāh, muhammadun rasūlu'llāh' 'there is but one God, Mohammed is the Apostle of God', is not to be found in its composite form anywhere in the Koran, but its two halves occur separately. It seems likely that the first half of the phrase, there is but one God, is the one to which Mohammed attached most importance and that its subsequent association with the latter verse was a later embellishment on the part of typically zealous devotees. Through his emphasis of a supreme, transcendent and all-powerful Being, Mohammed, like all the great initiates before him, was effectively purifying the minds of his people of the corruptive elements of ordinary polytheistic thought. Remember, six hundred years had then passed since that earlier great teacher Īsā ibn Maryam, had revealed all through his doctrine of the Trinity. In the Mecca of Mohammed's day the idea of the trinity had, in fact, persisted, but the very essence of this idea (i.e. that the Trinity was consubstantial and indivisible) had not. Mecca at that time was by no means an obscure Bedouin backwater, but a thriving centre of commerce and trade inhabited by subjective folk with subjective interests. In the dualistic minds of Arabia's general populace the trinity – the 'triple-octave' – had once more been dissected into separate, personalized deities, known at that time as the three 'cranes' (goddesses) Lāt, 'Ozza and Manāt.

That Mohammed himself was aware of the real significance of these three goddesses is affirmed by the text of sura LIII, 'The Star'

– a text which apologists of the extreme monotheistic school of thought have long wished never to have existed. Certain Koran commentators have stated that the occasion of the revelation of these verses was an incident – 'the affair of the cranes' – which is reported in many biographies and stories of the Prophet. Mohammed is said to have recited sura LIII to some Qorayshite tribesmen at a place near the Kaaba (the holy shrine in Mecca). While he was speaking to them, the messenger angel (Gabriel) brought an inspiration down to him, prompting him to mention the famous idols of the Arabs, asking:

> Do you see Al-Lat and Al-Ozza,
> And Manat the third idol besides?
>
> Sura LIII, 19–20

Two more quotations come after these, but they were excised from most of the early copies of the Koran because it was thought that the Devil has put the words into the Prophet's mouth and that he later regretted having spoken them. These are the original 'satanic verses':

> These are the exalted females [cranes]
> And truly their intercession may be expected.

According to one early commentary, the Prophet then knelt down and paid direct homage to them. Clearly the Qorayshites were somewhat taken aback by the Prophet's admission, which is evidenced by their alleged response as the sura continues:

> What? shall ye have male progeny and God female?
> This were indeed an unfair partition!
>
> Sura LIII, 21–2

To which Mohammed replied, 'These are mere names.' See also sura V, 'The Table':

> They surely are Infidels who say, 'God is the third of three:' for there is no God but one God.
>
> Sura V, 77

It seems the concept of the trinity presented something of a problem to Mohammed, who realized the Arabian propensity for subjectivizing and personalizing the Deity. This is probably why the favourable reference to the three cranes was omitted shortly after its first public recital. Thus, in sura IV, 'Women', after speaking of the apostle Jesus and his mother Mary, Mohammed again alludes to the dangers of polytheism: 'Believe therefore in God *and his apostles* . . .' (verse 169). These are my italics, inserted to emphasize the clarity of the statement, which clearly includes the apostle Jesus and his doctrine. But Mohammed, ever mindful of the idolatrous nature of his people, concludes:

. . . and say not, 'Three:' (there is a Trinity) – Forbear – it will be better for you. God is only one God!

The cosmogony of Mohammed's doctrine bears such a striking resemblance to Mosaic revelations that it hardly requires commentary. To quote but one example, God's creation of the universe in six days is reiterated eight times in the Koran:

Verily your Lord is God who hath made the Heavens and the Earth in six days – then mounted his throne . . .

Sura X, 3

This is repeated word for word in sura VII, verse 52. In sura XI, verse 9, we read:

And He it is who hath made the Heavens and the Earth in six days: His throne had stood ere this upon the waters, that He might make proof which of you would excel in works.

And in sura L, verse 37:

We created the heavens and the earth and all that is between them in six days, and no weariness touched us.

This particular verse differs from the previous two quoted, firstly in that it is now God speaking through Gabriel (Mohammed speaks in the three previous ones) and, secondly, that it mentions not only the heavens and the earth, but also the third sphere of existence, the space between the two. The reference to lack of weariness on the part of the Creator suggests that the next day, the sacred seventh, far from being a mere day of rest utilized for the purposes of a weak or semimortal god, represented the voluntary adoption of the passive, 'Muslim' role in the world.

> Say: Do ye indeed disbelieve in Him who in two days created the earth? . . .
> And He hath placed on the earth the firm mountains which tower above it and He hath blessed it, and distributed food throughout it, for the cravings of all alike, in four days.
> Then He applied Himself to the Heaven, which then was but smoke: and to it and to the Earth He said, 'Come ye, whether in obedience or against your will? and they both said, 'We come obedient.'
> And He made them seven heavens in two days, and in each heaven made known its office.
>
> Sura XLI, 8–11

In this final verse, two extra days for the making of the seven heavens are added, which means that the time taken to create the whole universe has now been increased from six to eight days. This sudden increase from six to eight, through the intermediary value of the sacred number seven, has caused much confusion among scholars of all ages; and yet, as we have seen so many times before, when one applies the strictures of musical theory as criteria for analysis, such puzzles have a tendency to vanish into thin air.

The Koran and its many commentaries contain numerous other clear references to the octave format of creation. An interesting reference to the famous 'seven heavens' is to be found in one of the most respected Koran commentaries, the *Tafsir-ol Jalālayn*, written by the ninth-century Egyptian scholars Jalāl-od-Din ol-Mahalli and Jalāl-od-Din os-Soyuti. Verse 1 of sura XVII refers to a certain journey to heaven which the Prophet made by night. In their exegesis of this text the authors of the *Tafsir* relate what the Prophet had to say about it. Although the story is unsubstantiated in the Koran, it clearly shows that the hermetic code remained the keynote of all Islamic esotericism. According to the commentary the Prophet said of his journey:

> That night Gabriel came, bringing a quadruped bigger than a donkey and smaller than a mule, with outward-facing hoofs on its feet. I mounted it and rode to the House of the Sanctuary. I tied the glistening bridle onto the ring onto which the prophets usually tied it. In the Furthest Mosque I lowered my head to the ground three times in prayer. When I came out, Gabriel brought two vessels to me, one filled with milk and one filled with wine. I chose the one filled with milk, and Gabriel approved of my choice. Then we flew to the first heaven. At the gate of the first heaven a guard asked, 'Who is it?' Gabriel answered, 'It is Gabriel'. The guard asked, 'Who is with you?' Gabriel answered, 'Mohammed'. The guard asked, 'Has he been summoned?' Gabriel said, 'Yes'. Then the guard opened the gate of the heaven. Adam came to meet me and said, 'You are welcome'.

Subsequently Mohammed traverses each of the other six heavens in a similar fashion, finishing his sojourn in the seventh, where he sees Abraham reclining in the 'populous abode' into which seventy thousand angels go every day and out of which none ever come.

But looking now at this text in the light of our knowledge of hermetic law, we shall see that its authors were true initiates – alchemists who were in possession of none other than the 'philosopher's stone' itself.

First note that the Prophet's journey begins with Gabriel and with the image of the quadruped, so the symbolic number four immediately springs to mind. This denotes the preparatory stage/ scale of the journey:

• • • •

Now this quadruped, in being bigger than a donkey and smaller than a mule, is therefore symbolic of a third, intermediary manifestation, thus giving rise to the next symbolic number of the passage, the number three. The relevance of this number is further compounded by the subsequent actions of the Prophet, who, upon entering the Furthest Mosque, lowers his head three times in prayer:

Next follows a piece of imagery giving rise to the number two, the two vessels, one filled with (alkaline) milk and one filled with (acidic) wine, which Gabriel offers to Mohammed:

Mohammed evidently makes the wisest possible choice by opting for the vessel filled with milk (an essentially feminine or passive symbol), for it is after this that he rewarded with entry into the first of the seven heavens:

As we can see, the whole text is yet another example of literary artistry of the highest order, describing, in symbolic detail, the successive stages in the evolutionary development of the tetrad.

Mohammed was much impressed by the great fast observed by the Jews on the tenth day of the month of Tishri, aptly called Yom Kippur, the Day of Atonement. In Arabized Aramaic it was called simply Ashūrā, 'the tenth', and the Prophet, who clearly acknowledged its importance, instructed his followers to observe it also.

> Truly the men who resign themselves to God (Muslims) and
>   the women who resign themselves
> and the believing men and the believing women,
> and the devout men and the devout women,
> and the men of truth and the women of truth,
> and the patient men and the patient women,
> and the humble men and the humble women,
> and the men who gives alms and the women who give alms,
> and the men who fast and the women who fast,

and the chaste men and the chaste women,
and the men and the women who oft remember God:
for them hath God prepared forgiveness and a rich
  recompense.

Sura XXIII, 35

In the Koran are to be found certain texts, an example of which is quoted above, which comply in form and metre to the tenfold pattern of the tetrad. There is also a rather interesting reference to the originator of the Judaic 'tenth', which not only demonstrates the Prophet's awareness of its true value, but which also throws light on an hitherto unmentioned mystery – that of the first Egyptian pantheon of nine gods, the Great Ennead. The passage in question is in sura XXVII, 'The Ant', in which Mohammed recites a dialogue between God and Moses. God is speaking:

Put now thy hand into thy bosom: it shall come forth white, yet free from hurt: one of nine signs to Pharaoh and his people; for a perverse people are they.

And when our signs were wrought in their very sight, they said, 'This is plain magic.'

Sura XXVII, 12–13

At first reading this passage might seem somewhat contradictory. The Mosaic 'ten' had long been one of the most powerful metaphysical symbols known to man, and yet here we see a quite distinct reference to Moses and the number nine, the ennead. There is of course no contradiction whatever, because the number nine *and* the number ten both refer to the same thing. The tetrad, as we know, is a tenfold concentration of 'resonance', but the pattern traced by the transitional periods *between* the seven fundamental notes and the two extra semitones is ninefold, depicted in diagrammatic form in an earlier chapter as a chain of nine links, or nine octaves, or sixty-four notes. In this respect it is worth noting also that the Prophet is said to have lived for sixty-three years, a detail which leads one to suspect that his final ascension to heaven, like that of Christ, may have been a deliberate, perfectly timed event.

The essential message of Islam eventually became condensed

into a single, rather ingenious symbol known as the enneagram. Derived in all probability from the Pythagorean tetrad of former days, the enneagram was employed by Islamic teachers to present to the trained and intuitive eye a living image of the harmony of the universe. It is comprised of an equilateral triangle and a six-pointed figure drawn inside a circle, like this:

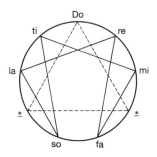

Taking the equilateral triangle as an expression of the law of three forces, we see that its apex (which, being a point, stands in relation to the line of the base exactly as does zero to infinity), marks the beginning of a ninefold division of the circle. The apex itself therefore denotes the first stage *and* the last, the tenth. If we note the position of the two extreme points described by the triangle's base, we see that, at the first semitone interval, between the notes 'mi' and 'fa', the necessary 'shock' is provided by the first point of the base, but that the second point of the base intercepts the octave, not between the notes 'ti' and 'Do', but between the notes 'so' and 'la'. This apparent illogical placement of the last semitone is a typical Islamic trick, a purposefully introduced error intended to remind the student that his work is never finished. 'And do ye not remember?', Christ asked his disciples on their day of little faith. The verb 'to remember' is the key here. The misplacement of the second semitone of the enneagram is simply a reminding factor of the true nature of the desired (psychological) 'shock' at the cosmic note 'ti', where a new level of awareness is realized, or remembered.

The enneagram is a masterpiece of Islamic hermeticism. As a cosmic model it can be superimposed over any evolutionary phenomenon, be it the human body, a troop of whirling dervishes, or indeed, a solar system like ours. To the alchemist and the sufi it is sacred; and its authenticity as a genuine work of art is beyond doubt. It is an octave, a tetrad.

When Mohammed instituted the Islamic hajj (pilgrimage) to Mecca he endorsed several of the existing customs of the Arabs. All the ceremonies of the hajj had been practised in pre-Islamic times and these were retained with only slight modifications. The heart of the holy shrine in Mecca is the Kaaba, a certain black stone of meteoric origin. The pagan Arabs used to circumambulate the stone and simultaneously call out the name of one of the three 'cranes', Lāt, ʿOzza and Manāt, or any other idol worshipped by their particular tribe. Under Islam the call to an idol was replaced by the call to God and the circuitary movements around the Kaaba were clearly defined in number, rhythm and sequence. The whole of the hajj, in fact, was modified in this way.

It begins exactly six miles from the holy shrine in Mecca. Here pilgrims have to divest themselves of all ordinary garments, they must remain unshaven, their shoes left behind and their only vestment a simple robe of wool. The total distance involved – six miles – immediately reminds one of the six steps leading up to Solomon's throne, of the number of years that the Buddha was pursued by the demon Mara, the 'heads' of the beast in Revelation, the Son of Man's fate on Good Friday, the Zoroastrian symbol of Truth and, last but not least, the number of lines in each *I Ching* hexagram – the cosmic note 'la'. If this analogy is correct then the shrine itself should mark the seventh stage in the process; and the pilgrim, in the manner of Solomon when he alighted on his throne, denotes the eighth, transcendental product of this most sacred of acts.

This first stage of the pilgrimage is a harmonious (tetradic) octave of human activity (designed, remember, by a 'musican' and therefore already containing the two psychological 'semitones' between the full notes 'mi–fa' and 'ti–Do'), so we once again have a representation in diagrammatic form like so:

1	2	3		4	5	6	7		8
Do	re	mi	*	fa	so	la	ti	*	Do

At the end of the six-mile walk the pilgrim has 'acted out' an octave of energy and form up to the sixth note, 'la'. The psychological 'semitone' required to help the individual over the first semitone interval will be realized through the (active) impulse of simple, honest faith, Christian love, Confucian sincerity.

At the note 'la', the pilgrims, clothed in the fleece of the lamb, reach the shrine itself. Here they must do exactly what Christ did on Good Friday; they must 'die', adopt the passive role, and so transmute up into the note 'ti'. The note 'ti' is also harmoniously composed, which means that within it will be found the psychological or metaphysical 'semitone' necessary to complete the whole musical process. This seventh stage, located inside the sacred mosque of Al-Mashid al-Harim, is the act of kissing the holiest black stone of Islam, the central fire of its life and devotion. This *black* stone marks the point where the seal is set, where the Same meets the Other, where *white* light enters fully into play. Follows just one, brief, devoted kiss and this first sequence of harmonious human activity is complete. Living art: the resonance or 'ti' passes into 'Do' and the pilgrims, faithful, devout, passive, receive their just reward. They are then both theoretically and practically in a transcendental state of being and so ready to enter into the next scale of initiation.

They begin by making seven circuits around the Kaaba, three times running, four times slowly (1). They then visit the sacred stone called Maqam Ibrahim (2). They ascend and run between Mount Safa and Mount Marwa seven times (3). They visit Mount Ararat and there listen to a sermon (4), spending the night at Muzdalifa (5). They conclude by throwing stones at the three pillars of Mina (6) and, finally, on the last day, as an expression of total devotion to the Muslim way, offer 'sacrifice' (7).

In the Christendom of Mohammed's day esoteric knowledge and forms of exposition had to go deep underground. The foundation by St Benedict at Monte Casino of the famous monastic order early in the sixth century occurred at the onset of a noticeable general decline in cultural and philosophical activity. The Dark Ages were about to begin.

But not so with Islam. It was vibrant, alive, full of the fire of faith and boundless energy. Whilst the Gnostic and Hebraic streams of influence trickled on in metaphysical rivulets underneath the mammoth foundations of the formalized hierarchy, the great saints and thinkers of Islam were busy developing new or resurrecting old modes of transmission. Numerous great Islamic works of literature were created at this time and the sciences – products of the many new schools – flourished as never before.

Islamic orders took on many different forms. Apart from the alchemists, of whom we shall speak later, it is possibly the Sufi orders founded between the ninth and thirteenth centuries which are the best known. The Sufi order (the name means 'wool', an essentially passive symbol), headed by a spiritual master, or *shaikh*, consists of disciples who receive the initiation which, through a long chain, is ultimately derived from the Prophet himself. Many orders exist today, but all of them can be traced back to one or other of those Companions whom the Prophet himself initiated, in particular the two Caliphs, Ali and Abu Bakr.

A good example of the Sufi school is the still extant Mehvlevli Order of Whirling Dervishes founded in the thirteenth century by the brilliant scholar-turned-mystic Jalalludin Rumi. Born in Balkh, in Afghanistan, the son of a prominent professor in orthodox theology, Rumi (1207–73) became one of Persia's most distinguished mystics. After disputes with the ruler of Balkh, his father took the family to Syria, finally settling in Konya (Iconium) in present-day central Turkey. On his father's death in 1231 the young successor continued in the orthodox tradition, but the sudden appearance of a mysterious wanderer, Shamsudin Mohammed of Tabriz, greatly influenced Rumi, who subsequently abandoned the orthodox tradition and pursued the esoteric creed of Sufi mysticism, in which he is popularly regarded as having been a supreme master.

The most characteristic feature of the Mehvlevli order is the famous whirling dance performed by the *fuqara*. (*Fuqara* is the plural of *faqir*, or fakir, meaning poor, 'poor in spirit'). The dance, in which each participant fulfils a specially prescribed role, is an outward support for their invocation, or 'quintessential prayer'. Preparatory training for it takes many years, for the whole is a masterpiece of animated precision and symmetry, calling for acute powers of awareness on the part of those involved if it is to be properly enacted. Nothing is arbitrary, everything is meticulously planned and executed. The initiate's speed of revolution has to correlate exactly with the various speeds maintained by the other participants, in addition to which each in turn is required to exhibit a specific psychological characteristic exactly at the given time and exactly in the given place.

A Christian parallel to this process of initiation has already been alluded to in the earlier-mentioned Gospel story of the five loaves and the two unforgettable 'fishes', the Vesica symbols used by Christ to explain to his disciples the secret of transcendental power. The two Vesicas demonstrated the necessity of introducing the two additional semitone 'shocks' exactly at the point in time and space where the respective notes 'mi' and 'ti' of an octave of human activity begin to evolve upward. These predetermined thoughts and actions of the dancing dervish are in principle exactly the same: they are physical and psychological 'semitones' purposefully introduced into living tetrads of human consciousness. In this way each participant is able to repeatedly receive, assimilate and subsequently transmit metaphysical 'notes' in a law-conformable and therefore fully harmonious fashion.

So it was that the Sufis and dervishes of Islam succeeded in keeping the real art alive. Like their Christian and Judaic forebears, they actually fought *against* nature and won – they forced their way through to the secrets of the Kaaba. Perhaps fortunately so for us, because these medieval alchemists of Islam and indeed the philosophers, mathematicians and astronomers of the day were to become the chief sources of inspiration for many a hermetic phenomenon in the West, where, apart from the amazing masonic projects of the mysterious cathedral-builders, earthly existence tended for the most part toward orthodox theology and the law for its impetus.

Prior to the appearance of Mohammed, the Arabs had nothing in the way of architectural traditions. Most of Arabia's populace were either nomadic – Bedouins – or they lived in primitive, makeshift dwellings. Mohammed himself is said to have lived in a simple mud-brick house with palm-branch partitions and curtains over the doors made of black haircloth. After his death of course, all this was to change.

The oldest existing Muslim monument is the Dome of the Rock in

Jerusalem. Built by the Caliph Abd-al-Malik and completed around AD 691, the Dome is situated over the sacred rock (*sakhra*) on the site from which the Prophet is said to have ascended to heaven. It is a concentric, annular structure consisting of a wooden dome set on a high drum and pierced with sixteen windows. The dome rests on four piers and twelve columns arranged in a circle, so that three columns alternate with each pier. This circle of supports is placed in the centre of a large octagon formed by eight walls, each pierced in its upper half by five windows. Between the outer octagonal wall and the inner circle is an intermediate octagonal arcade, the arches of which are borne by eight piers and sixteen columns.

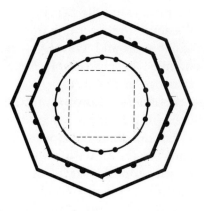

The Dome of the Rock sanctuary. This octagonal mosque is situated on the old rock of the Temple Mount, believed to be the site of the Holy of Holies. The Koran calls this site the 'Furthest Mosque', the place where Mohammed prayed during his famous night journey through the seven heavens.

As one can see from the symbolism invoked through the placement of four piers beneath a central dome, an essentially octagonal construction, the whole building is a precise masonic expression, not only of the principle of octaves within octaves, but also of the union of the square and the circle.

The Islamic streams of influence subsequently stretched deep into the heart of Spain, to Toledo, Granada and Seville. We know that the thirteenth-century English philosopher and alchemist Roger Bacon disappeared from his customary role as a teacher (apparently to Islamic centres of learning) and that so impressed was he by his Muslim contemporaries that he at one time turned up at the hallowed halls of Oxford dressed as a *shaikh*.

The Crusades themselves produced the inevitable rivers of blood, but they also helped to generate the initial impetus for the formation of the 'chivalrous' Order of the Knights Templar. The Templar schools, the result of a hermetic design which had its immediate roots in the Holy Land, would have been founded by those who were disillusioned or dissatisfied with the rigid, formalized dogmas of their own theologians and thinkers, but who were nevertheless aware of the true nature and essentially superior wisdom of their Arab counterparts. Perhaps in this manner 'faith' and 'devotion', concepts lacking the psychological nuance necessary to spark the Western spirit, became transmuted, as it were, into the concepts of 'honour' and 'chivalry' – impulses which, if properly expressed, must be inextricably linked with Christian 'love', Confucian 'sincerity' and so forth.

The great cathedral-builders of Europe, probably closely allied to the founding fathers of the Knights Templar, merely came, left their incredible marks, and then disappeared. They must have been initiates, for none but the all-wise of the day could ever have accomplished such stupendous tasks of masonic precision and form. Certainly the mystical splendour and sheer aesthetic grandeur of their creations, standing out so incongruously against the dark backdrop of medieval history, are products of the labours of no ordinary men.

CHAPTER THIRTEEN

Alchemists ancient and modern

God and the microbe are the same system, the only
difference is in the number of centres.

G. I. Gurdjieff, *Views from the Real World*

During and after the Dark Ages alchemy was the principal medium
via which the hermetic code was passed on by Islamic initiates to
their contemporaries in the West. In later years it was to harmonize
with the traditional Greek and Roman streams of thought and
thereby help to create the initial impetus for the temporal phenomenon known as the Renaissance.

Today, in the popular imagination the alchemist was nothing
more than a naive dreamer searching for a nonexistent
'philosopher's stone' so he could achieve the impossible: the
magical transmutation of one elemental material into another, for
example lead or mercury into gold. Alchemy is regarded as just a
quaint collection of superstitious ideas with no rational basis. It is a
curious fact, however, that the original ideas formulated by
medieval alchemists ultimately provided mankind with a new and
interesting approach to the detailed study of phenomena – an
approach which rapidly developed into the systematic modern
science of chemistry. Thus the rationalist will say that man has
refined the crude and simplistic alchemical principles of old into a
proper, enlightened and objective science. And yet, in the light of
legend, quite the opposite appears to have happened. It is said that
Hermes himself held that alchemy was a divine art, that it was *the*

179

supreme 'secret science' and as such was to be revealed only to the elite school of the 'sons of kings'.

According to the Old Testament, alchemy was first revealed by the 'fallen angels' of the Book of Genesis and was taught to Moses (in Egypt) and then to Aaron. The later Zoroastrian belief in a stream of molten metal purifying the souls of the dead also has an alchemical ring to it. In fact, fire itself, which was sacred to the early Persians, subsequently became the principal 'rare earth' of medieval alchemy. Later still, in Roman times, the resident scholars at the great library of Alexandria were suspected of practising the 'forbidden art' and even persecuted for it so, although the medieval Islamic schools are usually given most of the credit for its development, they probably derived many of their ideas from early treatises, now lost, but which in fact originated in Egypt.

In the Middle Ages intolerance to revolutionary esoteric ideas reached pathological heights. The adept had to behave very discreetly to avoid recrimination. Possibly this was why the old Egyptian concept of alchemy was reintroduced, so that the work could be steeped in the protective guise of allegory. The chemical symbolism was thus allegorical as well as factual, being used as a pictorial aid to the study and observation of all phenomena, be they atomic, planetary, intelligent, or whatever.

As one might expect, the hermetic formula 'As above, so below' was the keynote of the whole science, which involved the simultaneous study of both the astronomical *and* the elemental. Above is the macrocosm, the solar system. Below is the microcosm, the elemental world of planetary form. And in between is man himself, the middle factor, the 'mesocosmos', of the entire universal phenomenon. The medieval planet-derived descriptions of personality types still in use to this day ('jovial', 'saturnine', 'martial', 'mercurial', etc.) indicate that psychology certainly formed an integral part of the alchemist's art. Being an essentially musical discipline, alchemy involved the disciplined study of all three 'cosmoses' (or octaves) taken together.

The essence of hermetic thought was as clearly expressed in the alchemist's portrayal of the cosmos as it was in any of the other doctrines we have examined. The first law of nature, the law of triple-creation, was encoded within the combined symbolism of the first three alchemical elements or 'rare earths' (the three basic forces) of 'wind', 'water' and 'earth'. The fourth element of 'fire' is the transcendental product of the union of the three. It is the vehicle through which the whole phenomenon transmutes *up* into the greater scale above:

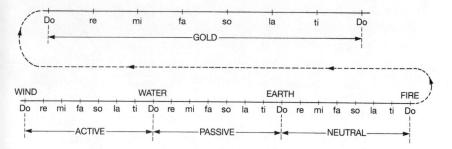

Once again a characteristic paradox emerges. At the present time we generally sit back and watch, in relative ignorance and in awe, our own twentieth-century magi as they busily engage themselves in the process of the transmutation of elements *down* into the abysmal depths of material existence peculiar to such as the curium atom. But this is essentially an involutionary process that, however sophisticated in form and method of execution, is always the same and therefore the very antithesis of true alchemical practice.

This true practice – the 'Other' side of the alchemical coin – was a process of psychological initiation through which the mysterious 'materia prima' (the fourth 'rare earth', or a certain and very high degree of metaphysical resonance) was ultimately obtained. As Jung expressed it: alchemy was an attempt to uncover the secret of the method of the transmutation of ordinary consciousness into the superconscious state of 'individuation'. So, one aspect of the science of alchemy is the Same and deals solely with the phenomenon. The Other aspect of the science is concerned with the numinon, that is, with the whole universal process, of which human consciousness itself is an integral (third) part.

The two primeval streams of creation (the involving world of material phenomena and the evolving world of intelligence or life) were sometimes represented by the alchemists as the combination of sixteen symbolic elements, two vertical lines of eight elements (notes) each; or two octaves, with the constant number eight, the square of which man was later to discover is the underlying matrix upon which the infinite variety and form of all matter is compounded.

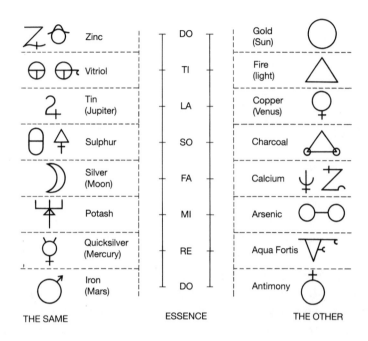

THE SAME		ESSENCE	THE OTHER	
Zinc	DO		Gold (Sun)	
Vitriol	TI		Fire (light)	
Tin (Jupiter)	LA		Copper (Venus)	
Sulphur	SO		Charcoal	
Silver (Moon)	FA		Calcium	
Potash	MI		Arsenic	
Quicksilver (Mercury)	RE		Aqua Fortis	
Iron (Mars)	DO		Antimony	

To the alchemists, the elements of the microcosm and the planets of the macrocosm were inextricably connected. The 'essence', or the spiritual being of the initiate himself, provided the crucial link between the two.

As one can see, fire itself, the seventh stage of the ascending octave, is represented by the equilateral triangle, a symbolized expression of the trinity. Gold, the eighth manifestation, or the transcendental product of the entire musical process, was suitably allied to the Sun and symbolized by the circle, the perfect ring, without a beginning and without an end: sealed, complete, individual.

Through contact during the Crusades the hermetic adepts of Islam would have realized that the concept of unlimited gold had quite naturally become an integral part of the peculiar psychology of Western society. Gold and its power was, after all, the real centre of gravity of the medieval mind-set. As such a potent symbol it was the ideal means of capturing the imagination of the people. You know, 'Turn lead into gold? Impossible! Surely . . .'

In this way the logical mind was elevated – even if only momentarily – above the endless yes–no interlude of ordinary existence. A man of philosophical persuasion may from time to time contemplate the 'philosopher's stone' itself, the heart of hearts. A beggar in the street may be hungry and cold and know great despair, yet thanks to the alchemist his restless mind can still be induced to ponder the achievement of the impossible. Lead into gold? Perhaps yes, perhaps no – but one wonders, at the very least one wonders. Not only that, such an idea would also have acted as a filtering mechanism, effectively separating the genuine seeker from the opportunist, so ensuring that only the truly poor in spirit (the *fuqara*) should enter into the work. Beyond this point the man steeped in dreams of limitless wealth could not pass.

Of all extant products of the hermetic tradition, there can be none which has been more abused and misunderstood than the tarot pack. Throughout history commentators have regarded the tarot as being a mirror of future events known only to the subconscious mind. This may be so, but until each of us can find some practical means of harmonizing our 'selves' with the forces at work on a different level, such fanciful ideas might best be left to the speculative occultist.

According to the writer Paul Huson the cards first appeared in Europe sometime in the fourteenth century. One theory places their source of origin in China; another suggests that they were brought to Europe from India by the Romanies; and a third – which the present writer is inclined to accept as the most likely – that the wandering Romany tribes brought their mysterious art form, not from India, but from Egypt. The word 'gypsy', in fact, as Paul Huson has correctly pointed out, is an old English abbreviation for 'Egyptian'.

In 1899 Oswald Wirth, a Swiss kabbalist and practitioner of curative magnetism, designed and issued a hand-coloured, limited edition of the twenty-two Major Arcana ('key' cards) of the tarot.

The edition was rather aptly entitled *Le Livre de Thot* (*The Book of Thoth*) – which suggests that Wirth's spiritual eye was at least focused in the right direction. He popularized the theory first put forward by another famous esoteric, Elephas Levi, that the twenty-two Major Arcana were directly related to the twenty-two letters of the Hebraic alphabet. Both were correct of course, but one is inclined to believe that, had these men fully understood the underlying principles of hermetica, then their expositions would not have stopped there.

In the seventy-eight card tarot pack we have the twenty-two cards of the Major Arcana (obviously a symbolized expression of three harmonious octaves, of *pi*) and fifty-six cards comprising the Minor Arcana. These fifty-six minor cards are numerically subdivisible into seven sets of eight; they thus represent the seven subordinate or inner octaves of the complete tarot design.

Evidently the pack was originally intended for use – like the *I Ching* – as a systematic, intuitive guide into the age-old mysteries of psychological harmony. The four suits, for example, are a numerical expression of the four fundamental base notes upon which the whole system is constructed. A contemplative attitude toward the random selection of the cards of the Minor Arcana would, in effect, impress the symbolic number four – the suits – into the subconscious mind. Having thus performed this first exercise in tarot- reading, the enquirer will have absorbed or assimilated fifty-six harmoniously interrelated 'signals'. Denoting the completion of the seventh subordinate octave, or stage of progression, this means that the seeker, in reaching this stage, has sounded the seventh, passive note in an octave of personal time – the cosmic note 'ti'.

The final note, or octave, is the Major Arcana itself. It is *pi*, composed within as twenty-two individual images and representing, relative to the Minor Arcana, the final eight fundamental notes. Thus we can see that, although the tarot pack contains seventy-eight cards in all, the true symbolic value of the whole set is derived, not by adding twenty-two onto the Minor Arcana figure, but the number eight; which gives, of course, a real value of sixty-four, the square of the constant.

As a final confirmation of the overall hermetic conformity of the tarot pack, we need only subtract the four distinct 'court' cards from

each Minor Arcana suit, for we are then left with a decad, ten cards
– the symbol of the tetrad.

In the West, the art of alchemy developed fragmentarily. It was
the new, occult (that is, hidden) form of hermetic transmission,
well concealed from prying eyes and grasping hands. Possibly the
alchemists believed in the old Christian adage about not casting
pearls before swine. But of course, then, as now, the 'swine'
would have been everywhere. In practically every age, the
Darwinian animal, en masse, has consistently manifested an
overtly superficial yet ill-disposed, eat-or-be-eaten nature. Their
choice of gold – the love of which has long been the root of man's
worst evils – as their key allegorical symbol shows that these wily
old-world chemists knew their contemporaries, as is said, inside
out.

But, occult or not, it seems likely that certain individuals that
have lived over the past five hundred years or so, although they
may not have been fully aware of it themselves, will have
succeeded in catching at least an occasional breath of the real wind.
One might say that the finely tuned or sensitive person is bound to
catch a breath; and again and again. Genuine hermetic strains,
remember, will not perish in our scale of time. Having been
'immaculately conceived' or 'hermetically sealed', influences of this
nature simply cannot die, cannot disappear from man's race-
memory and, so long as there exists a real form of consciousness in
which these ideas can manifest, there will always be those who are
able to discriminate and assimilate them. Hermetic influences – the
imperishable 'signals of Thoth' – are rather like metaphysical seeds
awaiting cultivation in the soil of the subconscious mind. As they
are continually received and transmitted from one individual to
another, they deflect and split off into subordinate degrees of
resonance, but the essential pattern, the underlying message of
universal harmony, flows ever onward. Nothing, in fact, can arrest
this irresistible metaphysical process, for such is the supernatural
nature of so-called 'divine revelation' that the message itself,
though its precise why's and wherefore's be long forgotten, can still
be transmitted subconsciously.

Even the ordinary, ill-educated peasant of fifteenth-century

Europe will have inevitably absorbed in some measure the hermetic symbolism contained, for example, within religious ritual, or in age-old customs, oral traditions, folklore, music and dance. Each of these essential human activities carries with it its own characteristic tone of hermeticism, its own particular appeal to a correspondingly empathetic section of humanity. The singular and all-important message at the root of all these practices may have been clouded by time but, as we have seen from our whistle-stop tour of the great civilizations of the past, it is still being perpetually transmitted to all, is still running directly against the mainstream of materialistic endeavour, and is still paradoxically blending, harmonizing with everything.

Obviously some of the more notable figures in modern history must have absorbed their fair share of this extraordinary metaphysical light. Adepts have appeared in many guises. The artisan and the scientist, the cleric and the prince have all joined hands in the quest for the Grail. Others have gone it alone, some of them through necessity (as in the days of the Inquisition), and some of them by choice.

Examples of enlightened individuals are numerous. The famous Elizabethan scholar and mystic, Dr John Dee, was employed by the Crown as a European emissary and was a one-time associate of Shakespeare. He had a lifelong involvement in alchemy and the psychic sciences and was one of the first Western minds to attempt an exploration of the intuitive realms through the oracular powers of a medium. His researches into hermetic traditions led to the first translation into English of the fabled *Necronomicon* (*Book of Dead Names*). Dee enjoyed great influence with Queen Elizabeth I and impressed Shakespeare sufficiently, it is said, to have been the inspiration for *The Tempest*'s Prospero.

Nevertheless, Dee left no clear indication that he personally understood the precise, objective scientific principles underlying hermetic traditions. This was also true of most of his European contemporaries and successors, men like Scottish alchemist Alexander Seton, Neo-Platonist mystic Cornelius Agrippa, alchemist and physician Paracelsus, seer Michel Nostradamus, student of Egyptian magic Alessandro di Cagliostro, philosopher Emanuel Swedenborg, occultist Elephas Levi. However, each of these charismatic characters must have felt intuitively that to harmonize one's inner world was to realize unimaginable possibilities. The lines attributed to Paracelsus, 'That man no other man shall own, who to himself belongs alone', clearly show that he was aware of the value of the principle of individuality. In Paracelsus' day, of course, one had to tread very carefully. The very idea of acquiring for oneself a real and permanent individuality was then (and, indeed, for the most part still is) a crime against society.

During the Renaissance the hermetic tradition was taken up by an esoteric school known as the Rosicrucians, or Brotherhood of the Rosy Cross, a secret society inspired by the works of Paracelsus. Many small Rosicrucian societies sprung up on the Continent during the seventeenth and eighteenth centuries, but most claims as to their origins and achievements are of doubtful authenticity and they remained for the most part fragmented and obscure, perhaps best interpreted as a passive reflection of the new active trend of positivistic science.

'Scientific', but unconventional, was the work of the 'healer' Franz Anton Mesmer. Born in Switzerland in 1734 and educated at the university of Vienna, he developed the idea that the planets directly affected the human body, via a psychic ether of all-pervading energy, whose flow was controlled by the magnetic effects of celestial spheres. Mesmer's most important contribution was his theory that human beings themselves radiated a kind of magnetic energy and that, by carefully following specific psychological procedures, it was often possible to increase its influence and thereby heal certain common ailments or deficiencies. Unfortunately Mesmer's experiments sometimes failed to bear out his claims and he understandably received short shrift from the established halls of learning. Nevertheless, he had discovered an hitherto unmentioned source of magnetic energy, generated not from without, by the forces of the solar system, but from within, from the heart, the solar plexus. This energy, the very life-force at work within the metaphysical phenomenon known as evolutionary intelligence, he named 'animal magnetism'. Of course, 'animal magnetism' has in fact been recognized as a tangible force from the earliest times. The Islamic Sufi regards this rarefied form of energy as being the supernatural product of a real and independent will. It is 'fire': the fourth 'rare earth' of the alchemist, the sacred creative element of Zoroastrian inspiration, the transcendental eagle of St John the Divine.

By the early nineteenth century the sacred laws of the ancients appeared to be well and truly forgotten, perhaps more so than at any other time in recorded history. While countless ideological arguments flooded the political arena, the principle of living out an harmonious existence along the line of time lay completely beyond man's comprehension. The typical citizen agonized for the moment to make money for the morrow and gave little or no thought to the past. Paradoxically time itself – the most impartial of all phenomena – became an enemy. To ensure the accumulation of wealth, time, rather than being accepted as nature's mediator, had to be beaten.

But time, of course, is not there to be beaten. Nor can it ever be. It is an impartial witness living under the protection of nature's embrace, an endlessly unfolding sheet of magnetic film stretching out and around the entire continuum. At every instant, as one beats one's opponent, or beats time, or makes a handsome profit at the expense of others, time itself takes a four-dimensional picture of the deed. These are our 'signals', these are our marks in the wider continuum; and these cosmic signatures represent what we are in reality.

However, the esoteric traditions that survived the materialist onslaught continued to conform to the original theme. The creed known as Theosophy was born, greatly influenced by Tibetan and Vedic beliefs, and bearing all the hallmarks of hermeticism. Numerous other such groups appeared and left their marks. Perhaps the best-known of these was the Hermetic Order of the Golden Dawn, launched into notoriety by Aleister Crowley, who, at his peak, despite his 'disharmonious' self-indulgent excesses, managed to penetrate meaningfully into the long-ignored depths of metaphysical existence. Not only that, through his famous adoption of the gematriatic symbol, 666, he effectively reintroduced a vital element of St John's masterpiece of Revelation back into the collective psyche of a restless, blindly evolving population.

A man who has had a more central and significant impact on Western philosophical and esoteric traditions is Carl Jung. A scientist and visionary of unsurpassable sincerity, Jung's contribution to psychology as a practical discipline is considered by many to have been as profound as Einstein's contribution to physics. His principal belief was that imaginative life was the most distinctive characteristic of the human being and that it should at all times be taken seriously. Armed with this conviction, Jung spent many years closely observing the inner world of his and others' dreams, discovering within them a whole new reality. He subsequently came to realize that many if not all of the symbols and images of which memories, dreams and reflections are composed actually had their own distinct form and existence in the spheres beyond time, in the subconscious, or the 'collective unconscious', of nature. 'Whatever the unconscious may be,' he said, 'it is a natural phenomenon producing symbols that prove to be meaningful.' Jung believed that such symbols of the imagination acted as signposts pointing toward the capital city of man's inner world.

Jung spent several years in the study of ancient alchemical treatises. A man of extraordinary perception and intuition, his view of alchemy is possibly the most sensible to date. He regarded his discovery of its meaning, which came to him after a series of premonitory dreams, as one of the most important of his intellectual career. He was at first inclined to disregard it all as superstitious trivia, but gradually he came to believe that the formulae were in fact allegorical descriptions of psychic processes, symbolic expressions of the mode of transformation of personality into individual essence, rather than simply the transmutation of base metals into gold. Jung found himself compelled to study alchemical lore for the best part of a decade. He evidently sensed, in a passive, intuitive way, that he and the alchemist were true kindred spirits, who in reality were dancing to the same eternal tune.

Interestingly enough, Jung's autobiography contains the suggestion that he himself may well have been a denizen of St John's unearthly paradise. It is a report of an incident in which the transcendental eagle of Revelation (or something very much like it) apparently manifested itself to Jung. What is more there was an independent witness present, who, although he did not actually see this mythical bird, certainly heard its call. While Crowley was experimenting with the fruit of the poppy high up in the

Karakorams, or perhaps frantically engaging himself and others in the obscurantist practice of tantric sex, Carl Jung was at home in Switzerland demonstrating to his one-time mentor, the arch-dogmatist Sigmund Freud, that the solar plexus was the source of a very real, emotionally charged power that under certain conditions could project itself well beyond the reaches of man's ordinary electromagnetic shield. They had been arguing about psychic phenomena and the older man's persistent scepticism was beginning to irritate Jung, when he suddenly felt a curious sensation in his abdomen, as if it were becoming red-hot. The incident then occurred. There was an extremely loud report (at which they both responded physically) and a sizeable section of a well-seasoned, solid piece of furniture standing a few feet away was split in two, as if it were a slice of parched veneer, by the force generated in the region of Jung's solar plexus. Freud immediately refused to accept the explanation offered, whereupon Jung first predicted, and then repeated, the demonstration. The two men parted professional company not long after this. Freud never afterward discussed the matter and remained very much the sceptic to the end. Jung, on the other hand, continued to put his trust in the eagle; he rode upon its wings, so to speak, and spent practically the whole of the rest of his life exploring the continuum of dreams, which he found to be literally ablaze with messages composed of light.

As I mentioned earlier, Carl Jung devoted much of the latter part of his life to a study of the *I Ching*, with its haunting, timeless messages conjured up by the laws of chance. But, of course, by turning to this remarkable book he had, in effect, arrived home. It was, after all, a route to the source of every symbol that he or anyone else had ever perceived. It was pure, hermetic wisdom and, in the consciousness of this one great man, it had finally achieved its preordained objective.

In the early 1920s a group of Russian and Armenian émigrés, refugees from the Bolshevik revolution, settled near a small town in the woodlands south of Paris. They acquired the lease of the Château du Prieuré at Fontainebleau-Avon, and established a community, the Institute for the Harmonious Development of

Man, headed by a certain individual of Greek-Armenian origin called George Ivanovitch Gurdjieff.

First created in embryonic form in St Petersburg and Moscow, Gurdjieff's unique school attracted some of the most powerful minds of the day. Notable was P. D. Ouspensky, the distinguished Russian mathematician and philosopher, who in his book *In Search of the Miraculous* provides not only a superb account of his eight years under Gurdjieff's direct tutelage but also clear evidence of the existence of 'paranormal' dimensions and a precise explanation of the absolute hermetic conformity of all so-called 'miracles'. Other celebrated adherents of Gurdjieff included the literary editor A. R. Orage, the writer Katherine Mansfield, the revolutionary architect Frank Lloyd Wright and the philosopher and mathematician John G. Bennett. Even Aleister Crowley made a brief appearance at the Château – though his encounter with Gurdjieff was reportedly less than fruitful.

Gurdjieff was born in Alexandropolis near the Persian frontier of Russia. After suffering considerable material misfortune, his once wealthy family moved to the now almost derelict town of Kars in north-eastern Turkey. Here, under the guidance from his father's friend, the dean of the cathedral, the young Gurdjieff was schooled in the disciplines of medicine and the priesthood. After this formative period of education Gurdjieff's unusually restless nature finally overtook him, and in the manner of all 'seekers of truth' he left home and disappeared, not surprisingly, into nowhere. We know only that he travelled extensively at this time, visiting the remoter regions of Tibet, Mongolia and the Gobi desert, India and Kafiristan, crossing the deserts and mountains of Central Asia to the Holy Land, Egypt and Ethiopia, including in his sweep Crete, Italy and Switzerland.

A full exposition of Gurdjieff's ideas is to be found in the literature he left behind, much of which was frantically scribbled out under the glaring lights of smoke-filled rooms in numerous Montmartre cafés, to be later translated into English by a devoted team of Russian and Armenian followers and finally delivered into the tremulous hands of the overworked Orage for editing. The complete body of Gurdjieff's writings (the whole work is rather grandiosely entitled *All and Everything*) comprises three major volumes. The first and second are further subdivided into three sections each, and the third, originally conceived of as having four sections, is in fact incomplete and was intended, not for immediate publication, but for reading aloud at meetings of his closest followers. Three major titles then, consisting of ten books in all, but with the final elements 'unwritten'. The symbolism is clear enough. Like Zoroaster, Gurdjieff has left us with an unfinished symphony, a literary expression of an evolutionary triple-octave. What is more, this hermetic system of division is by no means simply a cosmetic device, because the tone and content of each major section actually differ one from the other in exact conformity with the first law of nature.

The first volume is the active psychological force. *Beelzebub's Tales to His Grandson: An Objective, Impartial Criticism on the Life of Man* is a mammoth work of intricate cosmological and psychological wisdom presented in the form of a dialogue between the wise old space voyager Beelzebub and his grandson Hassein. Hassein is a curious little soul, and as they while away the time on their journey back to the centre of the universe, at his insistence they discuss in some detail the qualities of 'those peculiar three-brained beings breeding on the planet Earth'. Gurdjieff warned ominously that his intention in writing the first title was to 'destroy mercilessly' (how much more active can a writer's pen be?) all the ill-founded and fantastic ideas man has about himself and the world in which he lives. And he does just that. His penetrating dissection of our worst failings is enough to make any honest man burn with shame be he lord or beggar. But, in particular, his description of a day in the life of a 'free' man in society is undoubtedly one of the most chilling, real-life portraits of a prisoner in chains ever written. This is Brahma's book. The shock. It is yin, the first force, the Father chastising His child with a specific aim in mind.

As one might expect, in this volume is to be found a detailed exposition of hermetic law and the forces of nature, of the way in which the forces work, of the means of controlling them, and of musical theory itself. The elaborate and far-seeing science fiction setting of the whole epic is reminiscent of the trick first employed by Plato – that of 'tuning' the frequencies of signals to harmonize with the changing psychology of the evolving populace. Gurdjieff was a seer, a living hologram in a decadent world of endless polarities, who could intuit the pattern of future events with ease.

But then, not only does he expand the reader's horizons outward by taking a bold leap into the mysteries of space, he also 'digs up' the lost continent itself, weaving it skilfully into the tale to remind us yet again of that inner world, the inner tetrad: Atlantis. We thus have, on the one hand, an image of the 'transspace starship' and, on the other, a vision of the 'submerged continent'. As above, so below.

After this immensely powerful initiation, the reader is then invited to enter the second stage, the three books of *Meetings with Remarkable Men*. This is Gurdjieff's reconciliatory message: the neutral force, Vishnu the Mediator, the Holy Ghost, the Tao. This volume, of course, has a totally different tone from the first. Through these allegedly autobiographical accounts of his personal adventures, of his triumphs and failures, Gurdjieff now approaches the reader more as a friend, as his companion on his pilgrimage through life. Here we begin to get a picture of the man behind the stern, fatherly mask of Beelzebub the all-wise, and he becomes altogether more human. Subsequently we learn that, once upon a time, Gurdjieff was convinced that he knew what was what, that he could 'do' and could 'be', and that he was right in all his beliefs. Until, that is, he met wiser men than he. Three to be exact.

In this way we are informally reintroduced to a well-known Hindu concept (previously explained in the jargon of pure science by the great Beelzebub), that of the possibility of the development of the four 'bodies' of man: the physical body, the astral body, the mental body and the ultimate, transcendental product of the union of the three, the causal body. So, Beelzebub's first shattering call to awaken is now transmuted into the somewhat softer and essentially impartial tones of the three wise men who, through this idea of bodies growing from within, leave the reader in a distinctively meditative posture.

The third set of books, *Life Is Real, Only Then, When 'I Am'*, is the passive complement to the first two. It is an expression, in literary form, of the universal passive force: yang, the Son, the Lord Shiva. Now the reader is treated as an adult. The tone of the whole work is steady and calm and the words themselves, although they are often strung together in lengthy sentences, have a certain Socratic quality about them. We are duly invited into the adept's inner world, where valuable elements of his true spiritual nature are revealed. It is in many ways an immensely personal book, in which the author's innermost feelings for his wife, his aged mother and even for the Creator Himself are touched upon with clear and simple sincerity.

The fact that this third volume is incomplete inevitably leads one to question whether this was intentional or not. A promise Gurdjieff made in the second – to outline in greater detail the secrets imparted to him by the three wise men of his adventure tale – is only partially fulfilled. There are, however, details of certain 'cardinal' exercises (seven in all) designed to 'assist in the acquisition of one's own real I', while the reader receives persistent reminders of the fact that Gurdjieff himself 'acted out' his own life in a fully harmonious fashion. For example, he tells how he set himself three principal aims (one of which was to write *All and Everything*), all of which were to be accomplished in seven years.

This final and unfinished work, originally intended to consist of four sections, ends, rather abruptly, in the middle of a chapter entitled 'The Outer and Inner World of Man'. Gurdjieff thus appears to leave us completely high and dry. But, of course, if the reader genuinely wishes to know everything he had to say about man's outer and inner worlds, then all he has to do is make another 'super effort' (Gurdjieff's term) and turn once more to Beelzebub's scathing discourse. The whole story is there, even if it is couched in excruciatingly complex jargon and cluttered throughout with unpronounceable words. The reason for this is that Gurdjieff was in the business of transmitting genuine hermetic data out into the exoteric world, and he knew from experience that objective truths, if obtained too easily, would very quickly lose their power, fade from the reader's consciousness and disappear once more into the greater unknown.

There are definite prescribed ways to self-realization, said Gurdjieff. Each one of these is a practical means by which man can develop within a real and independent will. There is the way of the 'fakir' – of the body; there is the way of the 'monk' – of the heart; and there is the way of the 'yogi' – of the mind. Through conscious and voluntary sensory deprivation, the fakir might achieve in one month a degree of psychological resonance, of being, equal to that which the monk, through faith and spiritual devotion, might achieve in a week. However, the yogi, through reason and mental disciplines, may achieve the same condition of being in a single day.

But, said Gurdjieff, not surprisingly, there was a fourth way – the way of the 'sly man'. The sly man, it seems, knew something the others did not, an advantage which enabled him to compound the essence of the first three ways into a single pill and – presto! – the results, said the master, were instantaneous.

This system of the four ways becomes immediately recognizable of course, and we see that this was no arbitrary invention of a mere mountebank but *the* one and only scientific art of transcendental evolution. It was nothing more nor less than an up-dated version of the oldest discipline on earth; it was pure, twentieth-century alchemy. (Weren't those alchemical fellows 'sly' also?)

The trick of the sly man, the possessor of that elusive 'philosopher's stone', lay in knowing exactly where and when to introduce the necessary semitone 'shocks' into octaves of human development. We have spoken of this fundamentally musical process of initiation many times before. To know how to perform this 'trick' on another or others is art of a very special kind. For a long time the teacher himself has to use the power of his own will to direct the student. To this effect he will 'compose' miniature tetrads of activity which the student must perform repeatedly in time. The emphasis in Gurdjieff's system was always in doing, in creating, in fact, a living, pulsating tetrad of magnetically based energy and form.

In order to do, said Gurdjieff, paraphrasing his illustrious Greek forebear Socrates, one has to be. But, paradoxically, in order to be one must first do – deliberately, consciously, voluntarily. Then one is. One is being because one is doing, and not, as ordinary mankind has been 'doing' since time immemorial, merely reacting, like automata, to external stimuli.

'Choose an aim', Gurdjieff would say to Ouspensky, 'a small aim at first. But then make this aim your God. Let nothing stand between you and this aim you have consciously set yourself.' The realization of an aim, no matter how small, represents the completion of a whole octave of activity along the line of time. It has a conscious beginning, it has a middle and it has an end. It is, therefore, a whole phenomenon. Not just theory, not simply a vacuous dream in an idle mind, but a sequence of harmoniously composed signals of magnetically based 'intelligence' which, in being complete in itself, must also have its own, equally real existence without, amid the unknown reaches of the greater continuum.

We know from Ouspensky's account of his teachings that, long before man's endocrine system had been mapped out by modern science, Gurdjieff was already giving detailed descriptions, not only of the eight 'centres' and their respective functions within the organism, but also an exact exposition on the physiological and psychological effects arising from their interaction – always, of course, considered from the point of view of the possibility of their combined development into a whole, harmonious octave of 'intelligent resonance'.

In the first chapter, I referred to the work of a twentieth-century writer, Rodney Collin. His book *The Theory of Celestial Influence* is in fact an interpretation of history and the sciences according to the principles expounded by Ouspensky, of whom he was a friend and associate. I have found its 'musical' vision of creation invaluable. Collin's detailed researches into the octave format of energy and matter have already been mentioned; he also explored the possibility of magnetic connections existing between man and the macrocosm.

To begin with, he points out that each planet of our solar system has a particular and different number of minor orbital cycles culminating in a major cycle, and that, from their relative movements one to another, the whole planetary phenomenon can be identified as an extraordinarily precise cosmological expression of musical notation and sequence. Making an ingenious table of major and minor conjunctions, Collin found that, by superimposing these various planetary rhythms, it is possible to define a numerical sequence of harmonic intervals developing in time, each stage of which is marked by the major conjunctions of one or more planets. Further, he discovered that the figures derived from these interpenetrating cycles, if taken as vibrations, represent the relative values of the notes of a major musical scale. He concludes:

The octave, or the musical scale, is a notation, adapted to man's hearing, of the harmony of the planetary cycles, which in turn is an echo of a great law which controls the development of all processes in the universe . . .

. . . In literal fact, the motions of the planets make music for the sun . . .

The Theory of Celestial Influence (p. 81)

Collin then goes on to explain, in his chapter 'Man as Microcosm', how these same planetary cycles, through the effects of their varying magnetic radiations over the endocrine system of the individual organism, make music for man also.

The eight major physiological 'centres', or sets of endocrine glands, may be schematically arranged to 'spiral' out from the heart in an order that appears graded from coarse to fine or, as Collin puts it, from material towards immaterial. He suggests that, according to their relative distances from the heart on this 'spiral', they obey the same laws as the planets in order of their distances from the sun on a similar schematic 'spiral'. So, as each set of glands interacts with another or others, it not only transforms organic energy into the degrees of biochemical resonance necessary for a given function, but is simultaneously tuned on a cosmic scale to a similar instrument and follows its guidance.

Significantly, Collin has adopted the traditional geocentric view of the ancients and composed a fundamental 'planetary' octave from the seven spheres of the solar system which, under favourable conditions, are all visible from the earth: the sun, the moon, Mercury, Venus, Mars, Jupiter and Saturn. Light from the sun continuously circulates among these seven, its reflected variations directly discernible by us. The three 'invisible' planets, Uranus (which stands, in fact, on the borderline of visibility), Neptune and Pluto, are outside this particular scale of solar and planetary resonance. They represent the beginning of a second, subordinate planetary octave and in relation to their effects on the organism manifest their influence to a lesser material degree.

Collin's correlation of the endocrine glands with planets matches the thymus with the sun, the pancreas with the moon, the thyroid gland with Mercury, the parathyroid glands with Venus, the adrenal glands with Mars, and the pituitary gland with Jupiter and Saturn.

The sex glands are of particular interest. Occupying the same position relative to the heart as Uranus in relation to the sun, they are the only endocrine transformers that, under normal circumstances, can produce real and lasting, or transcendental, phenomena, i.e. children. These glands actually create, or conceive, and they represent a fully harmonious biochemical manifestation of the unifying interval beween the cosmic notes 'la' (male, active) and 'ti' (female, passive). Not surprisingly, this marks the seventh stage in Collin's ascending scale of biochemical resonance – the stage which, as we shall attempt to demonstrate in the final chapter of this book, proceeds through time and space upon the plane of light.

It is also notable that the sex glands and their macrocosmic counterpart Uranus appear to have (relative to man's normal powers of perception) one thing in common. That is, the sex glands themselves stand, as it were, on the borderline between the material and the immaterial (or the physical and the metaphysical), while the planet Uranus, in lying just outside our geocentric circle of light, exists on the very fringe of man's natural vision.

The final gland, the mysterious eighth, is the pineal, situated at the focal point of the brain. To the modern scientist the true purpose of this gland remains unknown. Indications are that its functions exist only as potential, and that it is connected in some way with man's psychic abilities. Its position in relation to the heart suggests that it may have a special affinity to the finer, 'invisible' (or ultraviolet) radiations peculiar to Neptune, a planet which, unlike the heavenly bodies to which the other glands are allied, remains ever beyond our sight.

Collin concludes by examining the findings of modern endocrinology from the point of view of medieval alchemy. In a well-balanced person, he said, the interaction of all these glands would be perfectly harmonious. So the ideal individual would be indistinguishable as a specific type. However, the endocrinologist – whose science, remember, is the study of anything but the ideal individual – has identified certain characteristics resulting from the overactivity of each set of glands. And, of course, if the magnetic connections between glands and planets do indeed exist, this would mean that, when a given planet reaches its zenith, the gland to which it is allied should respond accordingly. Similarly, an individual who had one or another gland highly developed would enjoy a special affinity to the appropriate planet. We thus have a means whereby the descriptions of planetary types used by the alchemical fraternity of yore can be compared with the findings of modern science. It is an interesting concept and, as Collin himself goes on to demonstrate, the correspondence between these two outwardly different schools of thought is in fact uncannily accurate.

CHAPTER FOURTEEN

Beyond the speed of light

'The shortest line', Einstein replied,
'Is not the one that's straight;
It curves around upon itself,
Much like a figure eight,
And if you go too rapidly,
You will arrive too late.'

Professor W. Williams, 'The Einstein and the Eddington',
1924 (Astronomer Arthur Eddington's 1919 solar eclipse
measurements confirmed the general theory of relativity.)

At this point it will be useful if we examine, from a modern scientific viewpoint, the age-old question of the sacred covenant – the phenomenon of light.

The twentieth-century dictionary definition of light reads as follows: the agency by which objects are rendered visible; electromagnetic radiation capable of producing visual sensation. The generation of light is currently attributed to the particle/wave existence of an elusive group of subatomic entities known collectively as the photon. The implications of this particle/wave duality, which we shall look at in more detail further on, is that light manifests as particles of matter in some areas of experimentation, and wave energy in others. A photon is actually the 'quantum' (packet) of energy generated during this perpetual and instantaneous material/immaterial interchange.

In the world of physics, light is a unique phenomenon. Einstein's theory of special relativity, which is arguably the most profound scientific revelation of the twentieth century, is based on the assumption that the *constant* speed of light is an absolute physical law. According to this theory, matter as we know it cannot move at speeds faster than the velocity of light. This singularly fixed law of nature subsequently gave rise to Einstein's realization that the constant speed of light – or, rather, the square of it – held the mathematical key to boundless energy. Mass and energy, he concluded, are simply different manifestations of the same thing – a fact which is summarized in what is probably the best-known equation of modern theoretical physics: $E = mc^2$ (energy = mass × the square of the constant speed of light).

The constant speed of light is about 186,000 miles – nearly 300,000 kilometres – per second. Fast indeed. Even so, the universe in which we exist is so vast that the light which reaches us from the more distant stars in the night sky is hundreds, thousands, even millions of years old. Yet still it travels; not slower and slower as time goes by, but constantly, brilliantly, and at the maximum velocity possible. So light never 'dies' (unless it is absorbed, say, by the retina of an observer); it continues burning as brightly today as it did when it was first created and freed from material bondage. The reason it can do this is presumably because of the speed at which it travels. Einstein calculated that, to an observer moving at the speed of light, time itself would not exist, it would cease to flow. This is why the photon can maintain maximum velocity and optimum brilliance, because at the speed of light it is free from the ordinary ravages of time.

Actually not all light is free to fly unhindered across the universe. The photon is classed as a gluon (a force-carrying particle) and it facilitates all electromagnetic interactions. This means that all matter, from hydrogen, the lightest of the elements, down to curium and beyond, is composed of photons and their associate particles, all of which have been condensed, through the natural interplay of electromagnetic, gravitational and nuclear forces, into a multiplicity of material forms. In reality, therefore, everything we can see and touch contains a certain and definite amount of potential light; it is matter in electronic state.

When a substance – any substance – has become fully formed (i.e. has acquired its full complement of electrons), it begins, automatically, to decay. Once the material absorbed electrons (and therefore photons); now, conditions permitting, it begins to radiate, to 'decompose'; and in so doing it is, as it were, returning its borrowed light. The fundamental particles of which it was originally composed are thus freed once more to continue their seemingly endless journey across space and time.

According to Einstein, any given body travelling at the maximum speed allowed by nature would possess what he called 'infinite mass'. As the speed of an object approached that of light, its time would slow down, its length would diminish and its mass would increase; but at the very moment it actually reached the speed of the constant, its space would be nonexistent, its time would cease to flow altogether and its mass would become infinitely great.

We thus have a current picture of the universe in which the two dimensions known subjectively as 'space' and 'time' have, as it were, elastic properties, the perception of which varies according to the relative speed of the observer. Neither dimension is considered as being independent of the other; they are seen as being somehow welded together into a finite-but-infinite, four-dimensional entity which possesses the peculiar property of being able to curve back on itself. 'Space-time', as this new universal reality is called, is curved by the constant force of gravity and is in a sense 'round', boundless but finite – rather as the surface of the earth is round, boundless but finite – but with four, rather than two, dimensions.

Given the curious fact that mass increases in direct proportion to the increase in relative velocity of a given body, the idea of a human being travelling in a material spaceship at the speed of light is wholly untenable. Physiological effects notwithstanding, there would be the insuperable problem of how to obtain and carry sufficient fuel to propel a ship of potentially infinite mass. However, if it were possible to defy the laws of physics and to travel in a vehicle at, say, 99 per cent the speed of light, scientists have calculated that for the occupants of the ship time would pass seven times more slowly than it would for the inhabitants of the earth they left behind. The passengers on the ship would become one year older, whilst those on earth aged seven years. (A worked-out mathematical construct of this theory is to be found in the appendix of a book called *Between Stars and Atoms*, written by the physicist Eibert Bunte.)

Now, what if we could go further still and build a spaceship that could reach something like 99.999999999 per cent, or a hundred millionth of a per cent below the speed of the constant? The effects would be interesting to say the least. Apparently, for the travellers themselves the difference would be nothing short of a massive quantum leap, for at such a velocity time would pass, not seven, but *seventy thousand* times more slowly than it would on earth. Three thousand-odd generations could have lived and died by the time our imaginary crew had completed a mere twelve-month voyage. Evidently that additional 0.999999999 per cent makes a vast difference in terms of our perception of space and time. At 99.999999999 per cent the speed of light, of course, the mass of any physical object would be seventy thousand times greater, which means that our hypothetical spaceship, originally weighing, say, 1000 tons, would ultimately (and with almost zero length at this point) have a mass of something approaching seventy million tons.

As one can see, the physicist's fact is in many ways as strange as the most imaginative of fiction. At the speed of light our ordinary reality literally evaporates, leaving the rational mind perched precariously on the knife edge of oblivion, never really knowing from which direction the next elusive particle might make its presence felt. Unfortunately, however closely we observe subatomic phenomena, we cannot catch more than a fleeting glimpse of a cross-section of the complete picture. The whole phenomenon is a long and intricate series of events involving complex manifestations of matter and energy in time. Science itself observes only that part of the phenomenon which happens to be manifesting at the precise moment of measurement. The shadow of the particle we can occasionally see, albeit only with the aid of massive particle accelerators, bubble chambers and so on; the wave is more elusive still, but even so we can deduce experimentally that it is very definitely there, inexplicably alternating with matter in an endless cosmic dance.

Clearly, therefore, the privileged crew of any vehicle travelling at the speed of light would experience an entirely different reality to the one in which we presently exist: no time, no space, no recognizable form. Indeed, if they were in fact existing in a sphere of existence beyond time – in 'eternity', as it were – then it would be almost as if, like the great metaphysicians of the ancient world, they had *squared* their earthly possibilities, so enabling them to traverse the physical universe as swiftly and effortlessly as the proverbial 'Holy Ghost'.

The idea that light itself might be the carrier of 'psi' phenomena is not new. (I'm saying, of course, that in terms of the evolution of human consciousness it is as old as the pyramids of Egypt, but we are here referring more specifically to the view of certain present-day parapsychologists who are looking for physical explanations for extrasensory perception, telepathy, psychokinesis and so on.) The photon is actually a small, discrete package of materially based energy and form which is transmitted through the whole electromagnetic spectrum: infrared radiation, light waves, ultraviolet radiation, x-rays and gamma rays. In view of the fact that low-frequency electromagnetic waves have a strong penetrating power, parapsychologists have proposed that the photon might in some way act as the medium through which psychic phenomena manifest themselves. As one might expect, solid evidence for this is nonexistent, so research psychologists naturally reject such an idea, their experiments having shown that electromagnetic shielding has no measurable effect on psi.

More recently the photon has been superseded as principal candidate for the cosmic role of Holy Ghost. Particles such as the graviton (conjectured carrier of the gravitational force) and the neutrino (radiated in certain nuclear reactions) have also been suggested. The most recent speculation has centred on an alleged particle that can travel faster than light known as the tachyon. The tachyon is a hypothetical entity and theoretically cannot exist, because special relativity itself denies the possibility of super-luminal (faster than light) motion. Parapsychologists are, however, presently considering the possibility that special relativity isn't quite the whole story and that psi phenomena, because they appear to disobey all known established laws, are outside known physics. Interestingly enough, it is the very latest theoretical concepts of physics itself which have inadvertently given a new impetus to the idea.

To follow the psi story further calls for a basic understanding of quantum mechanics, possibly the single most controversial branch of the whole of empirical science. In quantum mechanics, the condition of a particle is given by the 'wave function', which is a rather loose definition in that it doesn't actually specify exact values for a particle's rate and direction of spin, or its polarization, position or momentum. The wave function only gives the mathematical probabilities that each variable will have a certain value when the particle is measured. Since the object being measured and the probe being used upon it (i.e. another particle) are both of the same order of size and energy, the act of measurement inevitably causes the particle's wave function to react physically, by slipping from a quantum condition, in which the value of the variable being measured is indefinite, into a quantum state, in which it has a certain and definite value. It seems that wave-function variables aren't actually 'known' – not even by the particle itself – until one or another of them is measured by an investigator. Until it is observed, the particle is apparently in a constant and unknowable state of flux. Of course, once one of the particle's variables has been observed, the accurate measurement of other variables is automatically precluded. That is, we can never know with sufficent accuracy, say, both the position and the velocity of a particle; we can measure one or the other, but not both. This unavoidable element of uncertainty is what makes quantum mechanics so different from classical physics.

So, for the present time at least, the old, classical, deterministic view of an independent and objective universe is no longer valid. Subatomic particles inevitably respond when they are measured. Unlike macroscopic objects, which are unaffected when photons bounce off their surface structure, we cannot 'see' subatomic particles without altering their condition in some way.

Einstein himself had certain misgivings about the chance element implicit in quantum measurement. He couldn't bring himself to believe that God might be 'playing dice', as he put it, with the whole of creation. Indeed, to the end of his days he retained a conviction that quantum theory was incomplete, that ultimately a new form of determinism would emerge. His expectations have yet to be realized. In fact, it is precisely because of the successful predictions of quantum theory that the new technologies involving the use of superconductors and lasers have been made possible.

There is, however, a curious footnote to the story of Einstein's reluctance to wholly accept the quantum picture of indeterminate events. In the 1930s he and two colleagues, Boris Podolsky and Nathan Rosen, devised a thought experiment in an attempt to show that the accepted scientific description of subatomic processes was incomplete, that there really was some underlying unity keeping the universe in balance, and that particles do have a definite position and momentum, even when they are not being observed. The question posed by this experiment – known as the EPR Paradox after its authors' intitials – was startling in its ramifications, principally because it implied that, if the principles of quantum mechanics were correct, then some particles are in instantaneous contact with one another, even over vast distances.

The argument can be illustrated by considering, for example, two interacting photons generated as the result of the collision and mutual annihilation of a positron (postive electron) and an electron. Unhindered, they will each spin off along their respective coordinates to widely separated regions of the universe. It is known from the way in which the photons interact that each one will have an equal but opposite polarization; if one is spinning, say, in a clockwise circularized motion, the other will be spinning anticlockwise. Therefore, if the spin value of one of the photons is determined, the spin of the other can automatically be deduced. In the peculiar reality described by quantum mechanics, however, both photons are in an indeterminate state of flux – spinning both clockwise and anticlockwise – until such time as a measurement is made. Measuring the spin value of one or other of the photons causes its wave function to collapse into either a clockwise or anticlockwise motion, but because of the quantum correlations between the two particles, at precisely the moment of measurement of the first particle, the second photon must immediately react through a similar collapse of its wave function, resulting in a spin value equal and opposite to that of its partner. Both photons thus appear to be composite parts of a single dynamic movement. If this is so, then the process must involve the transmission of some kind of impulse from one particle to the other at superluminal velocities, a process for which special relativity has no answer. In spite of this obvious contradiction there is a growing number of physicists who are seriously considering such a possibility. They cannot explain how such a miracle might occur, remaining content for the moment with the results of actual experiments with correlated photons, which clearly show that, when one of the particles is measured, its twin, even if light years distant, somehow 'knows' the result. Contrary to Einstein's belief, therefore, it now seems that God does indeed deal randomly with the universe, that particles can act in violation of causality, and that objective reality has no place in the scientist's present fundamental description of matter.

Predictably the news that widely separate quanta might be connected by some supernatural form of 'action at a distance' has fuelled much speculation among parapsychologists. They argue that if, as quantum mechanics implies, all parts of the cosmos are connected on a subquantum level, then perhaps the human will may also be capable of employing this level to directly influence wave functions of quantum systems outside the brain. Scientific proof of such a claim is nonexistent, however, as scientists are quick to point out. They are prepared to consider the incredible idea of fundamental particles of matter having what amounts to 'tele-pathic' powers, but the suggestion that the mind might be able to tune in to a similar subquantum system of communication will not be taken seriously until it can be backed up empirically, if indeed such a thing is possible.

As we can see, the world of quantum mechanics is an uncertain place, a world of 'weirdness' (the physicist's own stock phrase for it), which bears little resemblance to the world we ordinarily perceive. In such a world time flows both forward and backward and none of the usual laws of physics apply. It may be that the arguments for and against psi phenomena working at super-luminal, subquantum levels will never be resolved. If such a pro-cess does exist and is nonmaterial, then it can't be measured to the scientist's satisfaction, so that should be the end of the matter. But, of course, even if we disallow the possibility of a superluminal form of contact between, for example, two telepathic individuals, information passed from one to the other at the speed of light would certainly appear as if it were being received instantaneously, even if the participants were continents apart. Light travels at around 300,000 kilometres per second. This is an incredible speed. It is so fast, in fact, that time stands still for me when I travel so. Just think, in a fraction of a second I can visit all the major capitals of the world and still be back in time to hear you finish saying that the whole idea is or is not preposterous. Ergo, beams of light move fast enough to accommodate most if not all of the conjectured forms of psi phenomena.

Obviously, if quantum mechanics theorists are right, then the velocity of light may be only a relative constant. To us mere mortals, as we go about our daily business here on earth, it seems unimaginably fast; but to, say, the particle/wave complex of the photon itself, assuming it had eyes to see, the plane of light would look entirely different, stretching out in every conceivable direction, a motionless, timeless, spaceless thing of radiance.

A quantum of light can be polarized circularly or on a plane. If it is circularly polarized, the plane of the wave displacement will spin either clockwise or anticlockwise; if it is plane-polarized, the wave motion follows a vertical or a horizontal orientation. This, at least, is the theory of it. The problem, as we have seen, is that the particle appears to manifest none of these qualities until we attempt to measure it, at which point it inexplicably 'jumps' and changes its state. What really goes on whilst the subatomic quantum is in its natural state of flux is still a mystery. It seems that the reality the physicists seek to grasp is forever beyond empirical reach. Every time they try to pin down the quantum structure under observation, whether electron, photon or whatever, its general wave-like properties disappear and it 'curls up' to manifest one or another of its particle properties. Furthermore, as I said earlier, once one wave-function variable has been accurately ascertained, all other variables can only be expressed as probabilities. The whole scenario thus appears to be one of almost helpless chaos, an indeterminate universe based upon a subatomic matrix of totally random, observer-created happenings, in which even God plays dice.

On the face of it, this modern view of the universe seems in many ways to belie the inspired vision of the ancients, who saw harmony and order everywhere. However, if one leaves aside the prevailing 'uncertainty principle' of quantum theory for a moment – for it has yet to be fully resolved – then we shall see that there still remains a substantial body of reliable scientific data which in fact fits in very well with many of the so-called 'religious' models of reality outlined previously in this book.

As I pointed out in the opening chapter, particle physicists have already identified the forces of the octave at work in the subatomic realm. The proton and the neutron, constituent parts of the atom, have now turned out to be just two members of a larger family of quanta consisting of *eight* particles known as the baryon octet. Similarly the particle known as the pion is now believed to be a member of another family of *eight* known as the meson octet. Then there is the photon itself, of course, of which the white ray and the seven colours of the rainbow are the most obvious manifestations.

The baryon and meson octet quanta are classified as hadrons, which are actually 'particle molecules'. Thus, although hadrons themselves are exceedingly small, they are by no means at the very bottom of the known mass/energy scale. The most recent observations have now shown that the most fundamental components of the material universe are particles known as quarks and leptons, the interaction of which is facilitated, not surprisingly, by a *third*, force-carrying component – the gluon. The primordial fireball of the big bang was apparently a superhigh-energy mixture of these basic quanta.

According to the current theory of classification, known as quantum chromodynamics, hadrons are built up out of quarks, which in turn are bound together by gluons. Each quark has what is known as a 'colour' charge, of which there are *three* possible values called 'red', 'blue' and 'yellow', after the three primary colours. The theory of chromodynamics implies the coexistence of *eight* other particles – 'coloured' gluons – which couple to the three colour charges of the quarks. Taken all together, these fundamental units of matter account for all the complexity of the hadrons, of which, presumably, there is an infinite number of variants. As we see, the pattern is a familiar one, and has been recognized as such by particle physicists, who have called this system of classification the 'eightfold way'.

Underlying this whole matrix of subatomic quanta are the four forces of the universe. All possible combinations of the *three* fundamental particles – quarks, leptons and gluons – are defined as the product of one of *four* basic interactions. These are: the strong, quark-binding interaction; the electromagnetic interaction; the weak interaction responsible for radioactivity; and the even weaker gravitational interaction. The gluon of gravity is a particle known as the graviton; three known 'weak' gluons of relatively large mass facilitate the weak nuclear, or radioactive, interaction; the gluon of electromagnetism is our old friend the photon; and the eight 'coloured' gluons provide the strongest nuclear, or quark-binding, force.

As the reader might recall from earlier discussion, this natural four/three combination of components and forces has long been a familiar theme in esoteric traditions, as, for example, in the form of the four letters and three intervals of the Kabbalah's tetragrammaton (the Hebrew name for God, YHVH, Jehovah), a symbol which in turn corresponds to the first two stages in the development of the Pythagorean tetrad – .˙.˙. – the seven stages of material creation. (The eighth, ninth and tenth stages of the process are applicable to 'intelligent' phenomena only and so do not enter the physicists' equations.)

Taken on our now familiar musical basis, these same interactions or forces of physics may be said to constitute the four fundamental base-notes upon which the whole 'random' symphony of matter is composed.

Physicists are presently wrestling with the problem of formulating a 'unified field theory', that is, a theory which could satisfy the laws of quantum mechanics and special relativity and which at the same time could mathematically accommodate all four of these basic interactions. The theory of 'grand unification', as it has been termed, has been successful in uniting three of the interactions, but the fourth and weakest of them – gravity – has evaded unification up to the present day. The conjectured carrier of gravity – the graviton – is an entity so small that scientists doubt it will ever be 'seen'. This is hardly surprising, because it is what is known as a 'virtual' particle, which means that it has no intrinsic mass of its own. This is why the force it carries is long-range.

At best, therefore, the graviton can only be expressed in theoretical terms, and this has now been provisionally formulated through the so-called and as yet unverified theory of 'super unification', which suggests that all the fundamental forces and subatomic particles are created from, and are intrinsically connected by, a subnuclear manifestation of energy and form called the 'heterotic string'. The structure of this invisible 'superstring' is theorized as having several distinct stages of development. The mathematics of the system suggests that there are exactly *eight* fermionic degrees of manifestation or modes of movement inherent within the string itself. ('Fermionic' refers to the 'exclusion' principle of quantum mechanics, which states that no two particles of the general group classed as fermions can exist in identical quantum states.) In order to account for the four-dimensional structure of classical space-time geometry, the superstring theory is further developed through calculating the free-fermionic formulation of the string in four dimensions, the mathematics of which apparently produces no less than *sixty-four* specific degrees of movement associated with it.

I could go on, but the detailed mechanics of superstring theory involves a language all of its own, inaccesssible to the general reader, myself included. The point is – and any lay observer can see this – even the most complex and advanced mathematical formulae of present-day scientific thought, taken as symbols, reflect virtually every aspect, every nuance, of the original hermetic code.

Possibly the single, most important feature common to both ancient and modern schools of thought is that they each have as the basis for their respective laws of symmetry the phenomenon of light. The constant properties of light constitute the fundamental framework around which the whole of theoretical physics is built. But remember, the ancients also looked upon light, or the source of it, as being representative of an exemplary or 'divine' order of existence. The Egyptian god Re, the God of Noah whose sign was the rainbow, the Zoroastrian Ahura Mazda, the Apollo – alias Helios – of the Greeks, the Holy Ghost and the seven 'spirits' of Christianity – all of these celestial images are symbolic expressions of the sun or its light.

Of all the major revelationists in history, Jesus in particular is possibly the one who most frequently identified himself with the light of the sun: 'While you have the light, believe in the light; and you will become sons of light.' (*John* 12.36) The Arabic scholar and student of the Middle East, Desmond Stewart, suggests in his book *The Foreigner* that the enigmatic cry uttered by Jesus in his final hour was not a call, as is popularly believed, to God, but a call to the sun. Mark's (15.34) transliteration of the four Aramaic words is 'Eloi, Eloi, lama sabachthani?' Matthew (27.46) transcribes the first two words as 'Eli, Eli'. Both Gospels agree that bystanders understood Jesus to have called on the prophet Elijah, or Elias. However, another important deity of that time was the Greek Helios or Elios (the sun), the vocative of which is Elie. Even as late as the time of Constantine the cult of Helios-Re was still so endemic in Syria that Christian preachers attempted to suppress it by substituting the prophet Elias for Helios. The suggestion is that Jesus's original cry has likewise been reinterpreted by Christian tradition and that what he really said was 'O sun, O sun, why hast thou forsaken me?' It was, after all, night-time by then.

As we know, the Helios-Re sun-cult had its origins in Old Kingdom Egypt, home of the Great Pyramid, which is itself a gigantic monument to the unearthly phenomenon of light. According to D. Davidson, author of *The Great Pyramid: Its Divine Message*, when the structure was nearing completion, the flaws in the visible casing stones were carefully cut out and replaced with accurately fitting pieces of limestone invisibly cemented in. The intention was to make the whole exterior absolutely uniformly smooth and plane, so creating a polished unbroken reflecting surface on all four casing sides. In fact, it was from the dazzling reflections from its highly polished casing sides that the Cheops Pyramid derived its original name, which is given in inscriptions of the Pyramid period, and in inscriptions of later times, as Khuti – 'the lights'. In Chaldee and in Hebrew, *middin* means 'measures', hence the Chaldee–Hebrew name for the monument Urim-middin – 'lights-measures'. In Greek this was subsequently translated as Pyra-midos, thence 'pyramid'.

To the ancients, therefore, light itself represented a divine manifestation of absolute perfection and power. And according to their so-called 'religious' theory of transcendental evolution, a truly enlightened individual – a metaphysical tetrad – would be defined as a form of intelligence which had attained for itself a level of awareness, of being, corresponding to the seventh evolutionary or cosmic note 'ti', and which would therefore be directly in tune with the covenant.

Theoretically such a presence should be capable of generating psychological influences or 'signals' which, being harmoniously composed, would have the supernatural capacity to penetrate *up* into a macrocosmic scale of existence and so *out* into a greater world existing beyond ordinary time. But then, this immaterial or metaphysical concentration of resonance, however subtle in form, must still have some kind of medium in which to exist. And remember, the finest substances we know of which exist outside the dimension of ordinary time begin at the order of materiality of visible light itself, the force-carrying particles of which are in a constant state of physical uncertainty, in suspension, as it were, in a 'timeless', 'spaceless' place. Perhaps such a dimension really is accessible to the properly developed human mind, the source of 'flashes' of insight, 'bright ideas', instantaneous moments of recognition and so on.The proposition is technically unprovable anyway, but certainly the early pioneers of human consciousness believed it to be fact.

The ancients also believed that man's ordinary subjective view of the world in which he lives is less than real, that ours is quite literally the world of *maya* (illusion), where things in themselves are not what they appear to be. This, of course, is precisely what the physicist is now saying, i.e. that all observable phenomena are invariably subject to the quantum mechanics principle of 'uncertainty' and so can never be 'seen' as they really are. Unlike our modern belief systems, however, the old science of enlightenment holds to the view that the true nature of phenomena can indeed be 'seen', but that the eventual outcome of any 'act of measurement' is dependent, not only upon the individual whims of the investigator, but upon his evolutionary state of being also, his inner harmony.

To see order amid the chaos, as Einstein did, for example, the investigator himself must first have made the grade; he must have acquired a certain, very high-frequency degree of psychological or psychic 'resonance'. As we have seen, the metaphysicians of ancient times considered that it was actually possible to 'tune in' to these intuitive, 'luminary' frequencies of thought through a systematic process of assimilation of harmonious psychological values which, once crystallized, enable the enlightened human mind to make the simultaneous quantum transition into scales both 'above' and 'below' – *down* into the microcosmic realm of the subatomic particle, or the human gene perhaps, and so *up* onto the greater plane of light itself. (As I mentioned briefly in the introduction of this book, there is in fact evidence in the final chapter to suggest that the human gene, or more specifically its host DNA molecule, is not only 'hermetically composed' throughout, but actually operates through and at the speed of light.)

In setting out the basic principles of special relativity and quantum mechanics to the accompaniment of the music of human consciousness, I have possibly broken many of the established rules of scientific enquiry. Even so, the very bedrock of human rationality is modern theoretical physics, whose practitioners are at this moment observing an unbelievably fantastic world in which law-defying miracles, far from being a rare occurrence, are actually the order of the day. The idea that some form of metaphysical 'signal' generated by the human mind could be capable of tunnelling through neurological space, backwards and forwards in time, might seem a little far-out, but no more so, surely, than the proposition that tiny particles of cosmic dust are communicating with one another instantaneously across vast tracts of time and space? As Einstein himself pointed out in a letter of condolence to the relatives of a deceased colleague, the real world is a dimension in which past, present and future are all one. Indeed we only have to look up into a clear night sky to realize that the past, at least, is with us here and now, for the stellar images we see reflect the condition of stars as they existed aeons ago.

But of course, this *real* world, be it 'timeless', 'spaceless' or whatever, need not necessarily be exclusively the property of the particle. Consciousness itself, however ephemeral, is also an integral part of the real world, so there is no good reason for supposing that the mind should forever be excluded from participating directly in creation's hit-and-miss game with 'matter', which is energy after all, something that every human being radiates in varying degrees from birth to death.

Albert Einstein is considered by many to have been the most influential theoretical physicist of the twentieth century. At the speed of light, or possibly even faster still, this man's highly-developed mental body made a momentous voyage across the universe. The journey ended barely a split second after it had begun, our time, but it was apparently long enough to enable him to conceive of the 'immaculate' theory of special relativity, the concept which effectively welded space and time into a single, dynamic continuum.

Despite the later, rather more fantastic discoveries in quantum mechanics, Einstein's singularly piercing vision of the reality of space and time has been justly regarded as the biggest scientific breakthrough since Isaac Newton discovered the laws of motion and gravitation. Nevertheless, given the many religious descriptions of nature's underlying structure outlined in previous chapters, one is naturally inclined to question whether the theory itself (i.e. special relativity) is actually a new and original idea? That is, did Einstein really dream the whole thing up, or did the whole thing in fact dream up Einstein?

The proposition may sound nonsensical, particularly to those who have devoted so much time and scholarly effort to the complex problems of science, but, in fact, if one takes a retrospective overview of Einstein's place in the cosmic scheme of things, it is possible to find elements both of his professional and of his personal life which bind him body and soul to the very spirit of hermeticism.

Einstein's parents were liberal, middle-class folk who loved music and respected learning. Jewish, but not particularly observant, they were content to send their boy to a Catholic school, where he encountered for the first time the powerful symbolism and ritual observance of a religious code. By his own account he was deeply affected by many of the aspects of Catholicism until, at around the age of twelve, he began reading books on popular science. Naturally he soon came to realize that many of the stories in the Bible couldn't be literally true. Somewhat disillusioned, he approached his thirteenth year feeling that youth was the unwitting victim of a deceitful state. Shortly afterwards he virtually became a school dropout, wandered aimlessly around Italy for a time and then subsequently failed the entrance exam for university. A year later however, the tables turned and, after a productive term at the Cantonal School of Argau, he obtained his diploma and in 1896 entered the Zurich Polytechnic Institute to train as a physicist. It was here that his attention first turned to the properties of the white ray and to the problem of what would happen if he could move at the speed of light.

Einstein's subsequent meteoric rise to intellectual maturity resulted in his becoming a legend in his own lifetime, but the prevailing hermetic influences which must inevitably have inspired him have until now been completely ignored. We know, for example, that the father of relativity was above all a mathematician and scientist. We know also that mathematics and physics could never exist in their present form without *pi*, so, whether he was overtly conscious of it or not, this ancient esoteric symbol would have been literally emblazoned on his mind. *Pi*, remember, is a sacred, 'magical' symbol, designed by adepts, initiated individuals who were in the life-and-death business of propagating the science of transcendental evolution. They knew that a symbol of such elegance and symmetry as the Sacred Constant would be bound to persist in whatever 'medium' it found itself. Remember, by their very nature, hermetic, 'immaculate' concepts are absolutely unique. Once perceived they may gradually descend into the inner-most reaches of the subconscious mind, but there, it seems, they will rest and wait, for a hundred years if need be, until they are watered and fed.

Having duly received and assimilated a sufficient quantity of these magical 'signals', Einstein himself ultimately succeeded in harmonizing his inner triad. Possibly it was only a momentary harmony – a single flash of intuition – but a moment's perception at the speed of light is by the physicist's own definition a *timeless* event; long enough, one suspects, to form an objective image of the dimension we now know as space-time. This was a remarkable achievement for a lone thinker raised amid the staid halls of nineteenth-century European Academia. Presumably the right psychological keys, or notes, had been struck in him during his formative years, forming a 'sound' base, so to speak, upon which to build the well-balanced man.

Undoubtedly he would have been directly influenced by his brief love affair with the Catholic faith, steeped as it is in some of the most potent forms of hermetic symbolism ever created: the incredible and dramatic Passion of Christ, the omnipresent Holy Ghost, the passive Mary, the woman in heaven riding to her place on the wings of a great eagle – and the Trinity, of course, the Christian *Pi*, a symbol which ultimately found expression through Einstein's intuitive vision of space and time being complemented by a third, invisible factor: relative velocity.

Although not a practising Jew, Einstein would almost certainly have been familiar with the legendary story of Moses and with the main features of Judaism: Noah's rainbow, the heavenly cherubim, the seven-branched candlestick, the Temple of the two sanctuaries, one 'above', one 'below' – all of which are essentially hermetic symbols, metaphysical signals which could very easily and naturally draw a thoughtful man's attention up to the constant light of the sun.

Then there is music itself, the prime emotional factor. Einstein apparently liked to unwind by playing the violin and was a passionate lover of the works of Mozart. The Greeks would have approved. An intellectually active scientist who can experience a genuine appreciation of great music is privately a person with a distinctly receptive, or passive, side to his nature – a necessary prerequisite, one might think, for anyone wishing to make direct intuitive contact with 'the Old One' (Einstein's pet name for the Creator).

Finally one should not forget that, as a physicist, Einstein must have been familiar with the periodic table of atomic elements, formulated schematically on the overall basis of an octave squared. He would have understood therefore – if only subconsciously – that the square of the constant (order of materiality) produces an infinity of variety and form.

Clearly, therefore, whether Einstein himself was aware of it or not, his whole individual psyche must have been saturated with hermetic data, with the 'signals of Thoth'. A sensitive, passive man such as he would in a manner of speaking have fed upon such data. They would have been his spiritual and psychological sustenance, and every time he chanced to absorb one or another of their otherworldly influences, it would have struck a harmonious note somewhere deep within him. Obviously the more of these notes that become assimilated, then the nearer moves the inner triad toward a condition of optimum resonance.

For everything its season, and for every activity under heaven its time:
a time to be born and a time to die . . .
Whatever is, has been already, and whatever is to come, has been already, and God summons each event back in its turn.

Ecclesiastes 3.1–2, 15

If this ancient Jewish scribe is to be believed, then nothing is new; everything has already been, has been thought of before – and this would almost certainly include the theory of special relativity. After all, from his formative education, particularly in the areas of music, mathematics and geometry, Einstein must have received persistent reminders of the fact that the key to infinity and therefore special relativity was none other than the hermetic code itself, the one concept in existence which can be used to perform a miracle – uniting the square with the circle, zero with infinity. Remember also, as we discovered when examining the inner structure of the Pythagorean tetrad, the three octaves of notes embodied within the formula *pi* are themselves subdivisible into three subordinate sets of three octaves apiece, so that the totality of 'resonance' represented by this inner formula would consist of nine interpenetrating octaves, or sixty-four notes, the square of the constant.

CHAPTER FIFTEEN

Life in harmony

Rather than believe that Watson and Crick made the DNA structure, I would rather stress that the structure made Watson and Crick.

Francis Crick, *What Mad Pursuit?*

The mid 1950s brought about an important breakthrough in the field of biochemistry. The discovery arose as a result of the brilliant work of the biologists James Watson and Francis Crick, who between them elucidated the precise chemical structure of DNA. DNA is often erroneously referred to as the 'genetic code', but in fact the code itself, which we shall be looking at in detail in this chapter, is actually the biochemical blueprint used by DNA in the synthesis of proteins.

As I mentioned at the beginning of this book, the internal structure of DNA provided the last in a series of symmetrical images which together gave rise to my own particular flash of recognition. Whilst studying its distinctive molecular composition, I came to realize that the genetic code was actually a biochemical manifestation of the hermetic code, and as such presented the observer with a living example of the transcendental power which can be generated by practitioners of 'objective music'. The practitioner in this instance is the humble cell, the microscopic biochemical factory which performs the miracle we call the creation of life.

The fundamental characteristics of any given species are transmitted down through succeeding generations by coded hereditary factors contained within the molecular structure of the organism. These factors are called genes, and signals obtained from their linear sequence and chemical structure dictate the evolutionary synthesis of numerous proteins, whose orderly interaction with environmental variables such as climate, nutrition etc. go to make up the characteristic form and function of the organism. The gene strands are called chromosomes, and they are thought to exist as particles within the nuclei of the gametes (reproductive cells) of all higher, nonbacteriological life forms.

The human body carries its genetic information on forty-six chromosomes. The whole of this information is known as the individual's genome. At first, this seemed to me to be a somewhat arbitrary number, particularly with regard to the central theme of this book. But then I saw that the chromosomes existed as pairs, and that one of the pairs was fundamentally different to all the rest. In other words, there are *twenty-two* chromosome pairs whose member are exactly like each other, and there is one pair that stands as it were in a class of its own, the twenty-third pair known as the XX or the XY. The Y is a relatively small chromosome and mostly doesn't contain any of the genes that the X has. However, the genes that it does carry are vitally important in that they contain the information necessary to create an organism of the male gender. When you don't have a Y, but two Xs, the result is a female.

In fact, the twenty-two pairs of similar chromosomes are called by the geneticist, autosomes. Autosomes carry mainly general, more simplified genetic data, i.e. genes which control the development of the less complicated characteristics of the individual, such as the colour of the eyes, hair, pigmentation of skin tissue, the size and shape of joints, bones, extremities and so on. The unique twenty-third pair of sex chromosomes may look outwardly similar to the autosomes, but in reality they are much more complex internally, in that they contain detailed genetic data which controls the development of a whole, integrated physiological system of sexual functions, including the placement and development of various organs and glands, and also the development of psychological and emotional tendencies related to sexual attraction.

Interestingly enough, any departure from this basic structure – twenty-two autosome pairs and one sex chromosome pair – results in some kind of mental or physical aberration. For example, if the twenty-first autosomal unit consists of three chromosomes instead of a pair, then the individual will be a sufferer of the genetic disorder known as Down's syndrome. Alternatively there are occasionally females who are born with only one X chromosome, or with three, four, even five. Invariably they manifest some kind of physical or psychological deficiency. Similarly males can be born with an extra X chromosome (i.e. XXY) or even three along with the Y. All of these unfortunates are infertile and likely to be mentally retarded.

Deviations even further from this human chromosomal-pair pattern of twenty-two plus one are found in animals. An extra pair of chromosomes, making twenty-four in all, results in a monkey; mice have twenty pairs, dogs thirty-nine, horses thirty-three, cattle thirty and so on.

Every chromosome is made up of two chromatids, each of which is an immensely long, coiled molecule of DNA (deoxyribonucleic acid). The molecule looks rather like a spiral staircase, with sides made up of sugar and phosphate molecules. Joining these sides are crosspieces or steps, each of which is compounded of a pair of nitrogenous bases, of which there are four: adenine, guanine, thymine and cytosine. Adenine always joins with thymine to form a step; guanine always joins with cytosine. The bases can appear in an infinitely variable order, and the order of the paired steps makes up the coded instructions which can be used elsewhere in the cell.

When the cell is ready to divide, the DNA must be replicated exactly so that each new cell will have the same type of genetic blueprint. This happens when the DNA molecule itself splits. The chemical units which form the crosslinks then snap on to the end of the split crosslinks, forming two identical new strands of DNA.

It is in this way that the genetic information in the chromosomes is passed on down through succeeding generations.

According to the biochemist, the four nitrogenous bases can

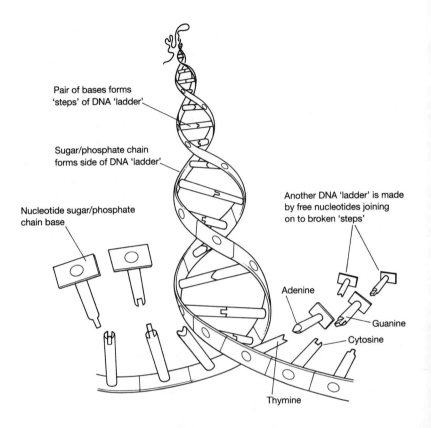

Pair of bases forms
'steps' of DNA 'ladder'.

Sugar/phosphate chain
forms side of DNA 'ladder'.

Nucleotide sugar/phosphate
chain base

Another DNA 'ladder' is made
by free nucleotides joining
on to broken 'steps'

Adenine

Guanine

Cytosine

Thymine

The famous double helix of DNA as described by Watson and Crick. During cell division, the entire chromosome unzips itself in the midst of a sea of free nucleotides. The two separate strands then automatically attract free and complementary bases, thus forming two new, identical daughter helices.

combine into precisely *sixty-four* possible nonoverlapping triplet-units, or biochemical codons, which correspond to the twenty amino acids necessary for the synthesis of protein, and also the two coded instructions for 'start' and 'stop' (production, that is). It is therefore assumed that the genetic code is highly redundant in that the generation of certain amino acids may be dictated by more than one triplet-codon.

Incorporated within the cytoplasmic material found inside the cell membrane and surrounding the cell nucleus is a substance called RNA (ribonucleic acid). RNA is structurally identical to

DNA, except the thymine base is replaced by the closely related uracil. RNA consists of triplet-codons of unpaired nucleotide bases and is the substance utilized in the process of formation of proteins. RNA manifests when a 'puff' is formed in the original DNA molecule (i.e. when one of the nucleotide chains separates slightly to form a loose loop). Unpaired RNA bases then line up and subsequently connect within the loop in the sequences determined by the temporarily unpaired bases of the parent DNA. As the loop closes once more, RNA triplet-codons are 'ejected' back into the cytoplasm. These are the templates, or blueprints, utilized in the manufacture of what is, in effect, intelligent energy – protein.

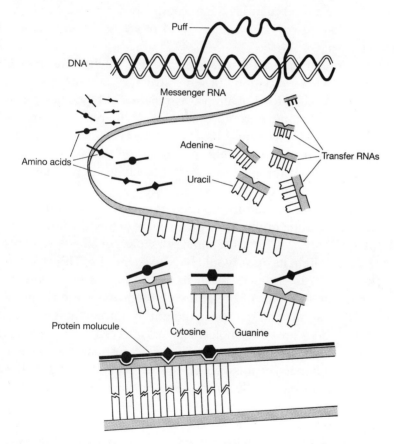

In the harmonious world of the macromolecule, fully resonant RNA codons provide the vital link between the bases below and the proteins above.

This 'messenger' RNA subsequently fixes itself to the sugar and phosphate backbone of each nucleotide chain (ribosome), and then moves along it, 'reading' the chemically encoded message. Another kind of RNA called 'transfer' RNA simultaneously carries the corresponding amino acids to the ribosome, which in turn assembles them into proteins.

Such, then, is 'life', or 'evolution'; it is a process of transcendental motion, through which inanimate particles of matter (the chemical bases) are somehow transformed into organic building blocks (amino acids) and thence into protein molecules, the most complex chemical components of the human body. To understand how this extraordinary feat of transformation from an atomic level of complexity to a molecular level is accomplished, we need to recall two other key discoveries in the world of science: relativity and musical theory.

Remember, the overall intricacy and length of chromosomes is such that possible variations in gene structure are endless. In a single human cell, a total of almost two metres of DNA lies coiled up in the microscopic chromosomes. DNA, therefore, from the point of view of the chemical base, represents infinite mass. The base (mass) is inanimate. DNA (energy, 'life') is animate. The difference between these two orders of biochemical resonance is therefore the same as that of zero to infinity.

Now, according to the physicist, energy itself is determined by the mass of the thing multiplied by the square of the constant speed of light, or $E = mc^2$. And by the same principle, for a body to travel at the speed of light its mass would have to be infinite. This implies, of course, that, in order to reach its next stage of evolution (to become an integral part of the entire chromosome), the chemical base itself must travel at the speed of light. But how can it do this? That is, how does the DNA molecule, or its host cell, cause millions of inert chemical particles to travel, or to resonate, at such a phenomenal speed? The answer, as we shall see, is that it does this simply by adhering strictly to the esoteric principles of musical theory.

Represented musically, RNA can be taken to be a biochemical manifestation of three harmonious octaves (bases) of energy and form, or twenty-two elemental notes. Numerically we can say that RNA triplet-codons are empirical manifestations of the developmental pattern described by the formula *pi*, with an evolutionary biochemical value of (number of bases) three. Each RNA codon has the potential, through one of sixty-four possible combinations, to produce one of twenty-two sets of instructions in the assembly of amino-acid-based proteins. Sixty-four, as we know, is the square of eight, of an octave, or the square of the constant. RNA then, itself an entity comprising three distinct octaves of biochemical resonance, must evolve through the square of one complete and harmonious octave of energy and form, to produce one of the twenty-two notes, or transcendental 'signals', comprising the three octaves of biochemical resonance at the next stage of evolutionary development.

What all this means, in effect, is that the constant or optimum rate of vibrations within a given triple-octave of biochemical resonance (in this case, the three nitrogenous bases) endows the particular phenomenon to which it belongs with the supernatural capacity to exceed the ordinary bounds of space and time, for having completed the course of its development to full octave potential, it can then transcend the scale of its origin and become, simultaneously, a single new note again, but in an infinitely higher order of existence.

The square of the constant – i.e. the optimum rate of vibrations within a whole, harmonious triple-octave of biochemical resonance – must therefore be analogous to the constant speed of light.

Just consider for a moment the phenomenal speed at which this amazingly accurate process of protein manufacture takes place. One red blood cell, for example, contains thousands upon thousands of molecules of the protein haemoglobin, and millions of red blood cells are made every second in the human organism. Surely it would have to be a process operating at least at the constant speed of light, the fastest speed allowed by nature, which could facilitate such a remarkably rapid and efficient means of molecule synthesis. I say *at least* the constant speed of light because it is possible that the finer, more subtle processes of transcendental evolution proceed virtually instantaneously, that is, one harmonious octave combining or merging with a greater octave at the speed of light squared, which is roughly ninety billion kilometres per second.

The square of the constant speed of light exists, presently, only in the mathematical equation quoted earlier: $E = mc^2$. But it exists, nonetheless, if not physically, then conceptually. And yet, special relativity itself excludes the possibility of matter travelling at superluminal velocities. Perhaps, then, there is some form of nonmaterial or metaphysical 'vibration' which travels – if we can call it that in the ordinary sense of the word – at the timeless speed squared. If in fact it were somehow attainable, then such a speed could rightly be considered as being of a supernatural order and yet at the same time one that is completely law-conformable, for if the tetrad *can* be squared (and we see from the processes of evolutionary development of DNA that it certainly can), then theoretically, being harmonious in every way, it can also be 'cubed'. This 'cubing' process – let's call it the 'tachyon vibration' – could doubtless never be identified or measured by the crude instruments of subluminal detection of modern science, but on the basis of the established logic of musical theory, it seems not unreasonable to suppose that it could indeed exist. Tune into the sun, so to speak, and you are immediately and timelessly in tune with the whole galaxy, the Milky Way; and if you are in tune with the whole galaxy, then, instantaneously, the world of all Milky Ways – the universe itself – is your true and rightful home.

The wider cosmological implications of all this are expanded upon later in this section, but first let us return once again to the microcosm and to the overall pattern of evolution described by the DNA–RNA complex. Diagrammatically the whole process can be depicted as shown opposite.

We thus have a graphic representation of the life-work of a genuinely illuminated being of the microcosm. The creature in question, as I said earlier, is the living, self-replicating cell, a perfected form of 'intelligence' which effectively receives and disseminates external stimuli in exact conformity with the pattern of development described by the internal distribution and sequence of the electromagnetic spectrum. And in so doing the cell squares (and perhaps cubes) its possibilities: it 'immaculately conceives' and so reproduces itself.

The DNA helix itself thus seems to function as the passive, or receptive mind of the reproductive cell, a concentration of 'intelligent' resonance which possesses, relative to its own unique scale of existence, full or optimum consciousness. At the crucial point of amino-acid generation (i.e. conception), DNA separates to form a loose loop, so allowing for the reception of external stimuli in the form of unpaired bases. Only by becoming passive, by relaxing the tension of one of its nucleotide chains, does it become possible for DNA to utilize this

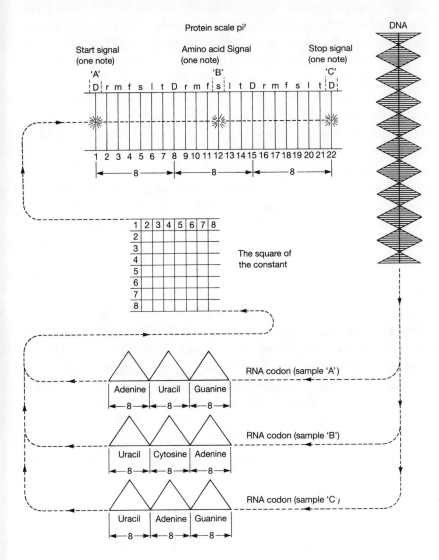

mass of external stimuli to proper advantage. Once assimilated and subsequently programmed, the previously random flow of chemical bases is ejected by the chromosome back into the cytoplasm in harmonious groupings of three, into RNA codons. It has now become a new and more intelligent form of resonance, which as a consequence has the power to find and lock on to the ribosome backbone and to read and follow the chemically encoded instructions governing the synthesis of proteins. For the cell itself, immortality is thus assured. Through the medium of light it is able to transcend its own time-scale (the maximum lifetime of an average cell is about twenty-four hours) and make a distinct signature on the greater body of the host organism.

If RNA codons are triple-octaves of biochemical energy and form, then relative to the same scale of existence, the individual nitrogenous base must be a single, tetradic (harmonious) octave, composed within as a chain of nine interpenetrating intervals. Like the codon itself, these individual bases manifest always in triplet form. That is, the electropositive elements combine with the electronegative elements, usually in the presence of air, and sometimes with the additional impetus provided by pressure, heat, electricity and so on. So the active elements at the higher end of the chemical spectrum combine with the passive elements at the lower end of the spectrum. Generally these combinations are facilitated by the presence of the nitrogen in our atmosphere, which acts as the catalyst, the third force. The single nitrogenous base is thus composed within as three subordinate octaves of chemical resonance, which means that the greater RNA triplet-codon, containing as it does three of these subordinate triple-octaves, is a composite biochemical manifestation of nine interpenetrating octaves of energy and form, or sixty-four notes – the constant squared.

From the twenty-two-note protein scale can be derived one fundamental octave of amino-acid-based resonance. That is, if we remove the two signals for 'start' and 'stop', then the remaining twenty signals should in themselves be a fully harmonious concentration of energy and form. We know that, in relation to the seven-tone musical scale itself, it is generally considered that there are *two* semitones between each of the fundamental notes, with the exception of the intervals between the notes 'mi–fa' and 'ti–Do', where one semitone is regarded as being left out. This gives us, overall, *twenty* natural divisions, precisely the number of amino acids employed by DNA. Such an octave, however, would, in relation to the greater evolutionary forces of nature, be incomplete. Lacking the two additional semitones it could never achieve absolute optimum resonance and so evolve further. But we know, from the orderly interaction of these twenty basic amino acids, that this biochemical octave does in fact – and in an extraordinarily harmonious way – evolve up to the next scale of evolutionary development, the stage at which the simplest kind of protein molecule takes form. This stage of development, or scale of intelligence, we can call the gene scale. Now, assuming DNA itself actually does operate upon the plane of light, then it must follow that the notes of the lower protein scale (the twenty amino acids), in being, as it were, orchestrated from 'above', will already contain the necessary semitone shocks required for future evolution. These mysterious 'shocks' are in all probability provided by the triplet-codons responsible for triggering the production signals for 'start' (active) and 'stop' (passive).

Most amino-acids have a molecular weight of around 130. The molecular weights of proteins at the gene scale of development appear to run in multiples of around 16,384 – a figure which, according to Rodney Collin's octave table of molecular weights of organic compounds in *The Theory of Celestial Influence*, is seen to be exactly *seven* complete octaves up from the resonance level of the amino acid and *ten* octaves up from the basic element, oxygen. Presumably therefore, both the gene scale and the protein scale are 'hermetically composed', with a difference only in scale. (I have mentioned Collin's detailed researches into the octave format of organic compounds before. His book should, I believe, be read by anyone wishing to consolidate their newly formed 'musical' vision of creation. As a tribute to his work in this field, it should be said that, at the time of Collin's research, the exact numbers of amino acids, chromosomes, base combinations etc. were not known to him. If they had been, he might well have identified for himself the true nature of the missing link between the inanimate and the animate.)

And so it goes on. As Collin himself points out, higher up the ascending scale of biological evolution we see that the structure of the entire organism continues to conform to the same hermetic pattern. The human body comprises eight individual biological systems, each of which is integrated and harmonized by the life-giving action of the heart. Each system extends throughout the whole organism, and over each, one of the endocrine glands functions as a kind of regulator, transforming the general life energy produced by the organism (from its intake of food, air and light) into the degrees of biochemical resonance needed for its own particular function.

This complete eight-fold system of biochemical regulators is simultaneously subject to three, mutually interacting nervous systems: the cerebrospinal complex, the sympathetic complex and the mediator between the two, the parasympathetic and vagus complex. Obviously these three nervous systems are simply a reflection of the law of three forces at work in the human organism; and the eight endocrine glands and their functions are in turn a reflection of the second great law of nature, the law of octaves.

It should now be apparent that this entire, 'immaculate' process known as the creation of life is simply alchemy in its purest form, the pattern of evolution employed by DNA corresponding in every way to the pattern embodied within the original 'philosopher's stone':

From the *four* fundamental nitrogenous base-notes, the DNA complex selects or programmes *three* of them at any given time, to produce *two* distinct properties (acidic and alkaline), of *one* biochemical unit in an infinitely higher order of existence, i.e. as one of the *twenty-two* signals at the amino-acid/protein scale of development.

Now let us assume for a moment that the ancients were right and that nature's evolutionary processes are everywhere the same, 'above' and 'below'. Certainly the various stages, or scales, of development of cellular life suggest that the evolutionary processes at work in the microcosmic world operate hermetically, as it were. But if this is so, then on a macrocosmic scale, the laws pertaining to the whole conscious individual would be exactly the same as the laws which govern the life and work of DNA. Therefore in the greater, universal 'body', in which perhaps we ourselves are but potential 'genes', the four 'rare earths', or forces of 'magnetism', would be the metaphysical 'bases' upon which, and through which, the finer processes of the evolutionary development of human consciousness proceeds. Man himself, in other words, is a cosmic 'triplet-codon', a 'blueprint', if you will, purposefully employed by some form of macrocosmic entity – but in the synthesis of what?

Following the lead of the revelationists, I have said that the four 'base-notes' of evolutionary or intelligent resonance are forms of 'magnetism', namely 'stellar' (active), 'planetary' (passive), 'solar' (neutral) and 'animal' (transcendental). Exactly what form these bases might take must remain for the moment a mystery. For my part I am content to leave the finer details of empirical inquiry to the experts. In this book, which deals principally with the general pattern of things rather than the detailed examination of individual particles and their corresponding wave functions, the 'rare earths' of metaphysics merely represent basic differentials of resonance or energy, three of which manifest in all of us in the form of our sensations, our emotions and our perceptions. It may be that these differentials are in some way related to the forces of particle /wave interaction described in theoretical physics, the most far-reaching being the curious force of gravity, which has the longest range, and which remains attractive or passive throughout. Possibly the metaphysical complement to gravity is the mysterious fourth base – 'animal magnetism' – which is also an attractive force with far-reaching properties. All this, however, is for the moment unprovable conjecture, the point being that the real basis of all 'science', whether nuclear physics, biochemistry or indeed metaphysics, is alchemy itself.

Taking the DNA analogy to its logical conclusion we must therefore assume that above or beyond the time-scale of man there does in fact exist some kind of macrocosmic 'chromosome'. This 'chromosome' can only be the starry world itself – or at least the great spiral of nebulae comprising our own Milky Way – an immense, cosmic entity which, just like its microcosmic counterpart, consists of an endlessly variable chain of resonating 'hexagrams' or suns.

The implications of this rather simple but dramatic assumption for all mankind are at the same time both awesome and profound, for if man/woman is indeed a form of metaphysical or cosmic 'triplet-codon', then this must mean that we in fact originated, or were created inside the macrocosmic 'chromosome' and then subsequently ejected by it out into the 'cytoplasm' – the four- dimensional, planetary world. Thus we quite literally came from the stars; and to the stars, it seems, we must eventually return.

As cosmic 'messengers', our purpose, as I have said all along, is to 'resonate at optimum frequencies' and so acquire the psychological or psychic power to enable us to carry our own individual 'signals' over to the macrocosmic 'ribosome'. Only in this way can the greater cosmic organism grow and remain vibrant. Just as the helix below needs RNA codons to assemble vital amino acids into protein chains, then so too must the helix above need our 'signals' to sustain and reinforce itself. Man's consciousness is therefore essential to this great galactic being, who appears to rely as much on us as we do on him, her, or it.

If the galaxy is a 'chromosome', then our chromosomes, on a microcosmic scale, are 'galaxies'. That is, on the scale of the helices below we are each of us a 'universe' in itself, whereas on the scale of the helix above we are very tiny indeed, proportionally equivalent to the minuscule triplet-codon in relation to the massive, two-metre-long DNA macromolecules. Beyond the galaxy, of course, is the Absolute scale, that of the universe in its entirety. Here, the mighty galaxy now shrinks to the size of a mere cell in the body of some infinitely greater entity, whilst the humble triplet-codon – you or I – is reduced to a single, transcendental 'note' in this seemingly endless symphony of creation.

The apparent insignificance of such a lowly level of existence may at first seem rather daunting, but in fact, as we shall see a little further on, there are further possibilities through which wider and more immediate vistas may be open to us. But first we must grasp the full implications of the DNA analogy, which suggests that the whole universe, far from being simply an entropic, expanding mass of galaxies, stars, black holes or whatever, is animate, organic, a living, breathing, sentient being.

In terms of our ordinary way of thinking it is virtually impossible to visualize the kind of 'body' such a being might possess, for its form transcends all space and time. However, if we assume that scales below are in fact repetitions or images of scales above, then we can perhaps simplify the picture if we regard the universe itself (that is, our universe; there may be others) as being something akin to a perfected, multidimensional version of ourselves, possibly with a 'heart' or 'solar plexus' that somehow feels everything, a 'body' that senses everything, and a 'mind' that conceives of everything. All at once. Furthermore, if the 'cells' which go to make up this unimaginably vast living form are in essence similar to our own, then presumably they too would have the inherent capacity to self-replicate. Thus, exactly like the great 'luminous egg' of the old Vedic creation myth, each of the billions of galactic helices which go to make up the body of the universe, having successfully evolved up to a condition of optimum resonance, would ultimately split its 'cosmic DNA', divide itself into two new daughter helices (each being an exact copy of its parent) and so continue to exist in virtual perpetuity.

Now we ourselves, remember, are as individual 'universes', each of us hosting billions upon billions of 'galaxies' (chromosomes) and countless trillions of 'immaculately conceived' entities (triplet-codons). And, of course, as we established earlier, the single, all-important factor which unites all of these microcosmic entities, great and small, into an harmonious whole, is that they are all of them operatives upon the plane of light. It will help to bear this crucial fact in mind as we now take a closer look at the way human consciousness itself might 'self-replicate' and so become fully integrated into the greater universal process.

So far we have identified three quite distinct spheres, or scales of existence: the universal or Absolute scale, the macrocosmic or galactic scale, and the microcosmic, earthly or DNA scale. But there is also one other major scale relating man to the wider continuum which we have yet to consider, and this is the mesocosmic, 'solar' scale, the one to which we are all temporarily allied. In this scale man is not just a single 'triplet-codon', nor yet a whole host of 'galaxies' (chromosomes), but a single, individual cell in the greater body of some kind of intermediate being.

Every cell contains a nucleus and, of course, a helix, or set of helices. The 'helix' in this instance, I suspect, is the human brain, the seat of this thing we call consciousness, the missing link between things above and below. The brain is an endlessly variable conglomerate of resonating 'hexagrams' (cells, neurons), which, like DNA, contains within it the coded instructions necessary for the production of higher, finer substances. And the way to program these instructions, as we have seen, is to still the mind, to relax the tension of one of the brain's 'nucleotide chains' (the hemisphere controlling logical functions), thus allowing for the subconscious reception of external stimuli, impressions coming from 'out there', in the cytoplasmic world of four dimensions, of planets and time and space and, of course, light.

A busy mind is closed, 'ponderous' and can receive very little. It may stumble across things of objective value from time to time, but only rarely and by chance. A passive mind, however, is an open one and so can receive light-bearing stimuli in large doses. The assimilation of these stimuli is an alchemical process which in fact alters the very composition of the mind. It builds it up, so to speak, reinforces it and ultimately endows the individual with the power to transmit metaphysical light, not only out into the greater sphere of the collective human psyche, but also over to some form of mesocosmic 'ribosome', where presumably it is then asssembled into something else.

We thus have a mesocosmic realm in which exist billions of 'chromosomes' (human brains) which are theoretically capable of assimilating 'unpaired bases' (i.e. converting impressions into conceptions) and then transmitting them back out into the 'cytoplasm' (the world in time) to do their very important thing. This thing that they do would obviously be the metaphysical equivalent to protein-building.

We know that, in the human cell, the amino acids are linked together by the ribosomal RNA into protein chains, acid joining on to alkali, joining on to acid and so on. Now if the same process is operable in the spheres of human consciousness, then it must follow that metaphysical 'codons' which have been generated harmoniously (i.e. according to the principles of transcendental evolution), would also strike signals up into a higher scale of existence. These 'signals' – we can call them the 'amino acids' of the mesocosm – would then form together into celestial 'protein chains', with light itself in some mysterious way linking up with consciousness, linking up with light again and so on in continuous streams of life-building energy.

Now in DNA the initial synthesis of proteins is linear and therefore one-dimensional. As the protein develops, however, enzymes catalyse an intricate folding process, so that the resulting protein macromolecule, having been folded many times over, takes on a three-dimensional form. Now try to imagine a similar process operating on the same scale as our mesocosmic helix, the human brain.

Despite the fact that man has a three-dimensional body, when viewed in the *fourth* dimension (time), he is as a point moving along a line. As he moves along this line he is (or should be) generating 'codons', or signals of consciousness which, together with complementary light impulses, are somehow linked together in a long, radiant chain. The 'proteins' thus formed (in time) would then, with the help of some sort of cosmic catalyst, fold up into a 'solid' form. But time is a line, or so it appears, so how can these metaphysical 'proteins', which have developed in a temporal or linear fashion, 'fold up'? The answer, as I have intimated many times, is that this folding process must operate *outside* time.

Imagine the line of time moving at right angles to itself. The activation of this movement would describe a plane. This is the 'timeless' plane of light, the *fifth* dimension. Now picture this plane moving in another, quite different, direction, say, perpendicular to its surface. We have now traced a solid, but with *six*, rather than three dimensions. I suggest that it is in these two higher dimensions – the fifth and the sixth – where the life-building 'proteins' of our spiritual bodies, if they existed, would function and develop.

In modern astrophysics, many more dimensions than six are presently being postulated. Stephen Hawking has suggested that there could be as many as eleven, the higher dimensions diminishing in size to the point where the smallest of them would curve up into a space measured in billionths of a nanometre (a nanometre is a thousand millionths of a metre). The wavelength of visible light itself is about half a micron (a millionth of a metre) long, which is millions of times larger than the proposed size of the smallest dimension. Of course electron microscopes operate with high- energy electron beams of wavelengths millions of times smaller than that of light, but even with this kind of concentrated energy probe, it is doubtful whether any kind of subquantum entity existing within such a small, curved space could ever be 'seen'.

I am personally inclined to the view that the six dimensions mentioned earlier mark the boundaries of our conceptual existence, and that the speed of the constant, and the square of it, will for a long time to come remain the yardsticks by which they may be measured. Of course there may also be a *seventh* dimension; in fact one would expect this, but it would be such an abstruse reality that we should never be able to describe it in common and understandable terms.

At any rate, within the framework of the reality we are currently blessed with, the way to a seventh dimension, or indeed to the sixth, has to be through the fifth, through the intermediary powers of our old friend and ally, the omnipresent Holy Ghost.

Throughout this book I have constantly made reference to our own sun and its light, the suggestion being that it (light) and consciousness are, potentially at least, opposite sides of the same metaphysical coin. The plane of light, it seems, is a dimension which is accessible to us. This is the 'book of life' of the Christian Lamb, in which are recorded the names – the cosmic signatures – of the truly literate of the members of the human race. Obviously this unique process of *un*-natural selection involves a form of 'writing' somewhat different to the one we are all familiar with, a form which may in fact remind the reader of the extraordinary activities of a certain, altogether remarkable 'scribe' who made a visitation to this lowly planet of ours almost five thousand years ago.

According to legend, Thoth, the father of Egyptian metaphysics, was the inventor of writing, the 'scribe of the gods'.

236

It is known, however, that the practice of making inscriptions on tablets of clay originated in Sumerian cultures long before the Great Pyramid was constructed, so rather than being the conventional art we know today, the writing in question can only have been alchemy itself, the 'divine' art of transcendental evolution.

In actual fact, there exists no teaching known to man, from the oldest scriptures right through to the modern paper on biochemistry or nuclear physics, which in any way either contradicts or supersedes the knowledge at the root of this extraordinary life science. The kernel of this science is the imperishable hermetic code; it is *pi*, an 'immaculate' esoteric concept which has actually served as the principal guiding light of the rational human intellect for over four and a half thousand years. This in itself is remarkable enough, but such is the unique nature of the hermetic code that it is in essence much more than a mere tool of the intellect. The symmetry of composition of the formula *pi* constitutes an exact scientific description of *the* optimum metaphysical frequency, a perfect, psychological wavelength accessible to anyone who genuinely wishes to break free from the interminable karmic wheel of 'natural', selective evolution. The 'signals of Thoth' are an escape route to heaven, the very life-blood of the human soul; they are the medium through which evolutionary consciousness must pass to realize its full cosmic potential.

As we have seen, every major spiritual leader in history has unfailingly regarded the hermetic code as being an embodiment of a complete system of conduct and development, a clearly defined musical discipline through which it was considered possible to generate within oneself the transcendental fourth base – 'animal magnetism', the 'fire' of the alchemist, the eagle of Revelation.

So the Noble Truths of Buddha, Zoroaster's metallic ages, the forty-year exile of the Jews, Mohammed's slow circuits around the Kaaba, the four Gospels, the four Vedas, the suits of the Tarot, the Hsiang of the *I Ching*, the four ways of Gurdjieff . . . all this is *music*, composed and skilfully conducted by those who understood that the transcendental fourth base of a metaphysical tetrad enabled the given individual to evolve. Firstly, into a properly tuned transmitter and receiver of the three life

principles (the three 'outer' streams of celestial or magnetic influence); secondly, into two, perfectly balanced coordinates of
one and the same phenomenon (consciousness/light); and thirdly,
into a transcendental note or 'gene', a real and lasting signature or
feature, perhaps on the 'face', or even in the 'mind', of an infinitely
greater, intergalactic tetrad.

Postscript

When the full extent of the hermetic phenomenon first dawned on me, in the summer of 1984, I had no real idea as to what I should do about it. I was very excited at the time, because I knew straight away that I had stumbled across something big, something of vital importance to us all, but I did not, at first, visualize a whole book on the subject, least of all one with my name on the cover. So much for my initial lack of foresight.

I must confess that compiling a survey on such a far-reaching theme hasn't been easy. I have had to backtrack many times in order to make sense of it all, but, thanks mainly to the inexhaustible patience and continual support of my wife, who in between raising three lively girls has found time to translate the bulk of the manuscript from the original Martian into English, an overall picture has finally emerged. All that remains for me to do now is to reflect upon it.

I suppose the first thing that springs to mind at this particular moment is the inevitable conclusion I have ultimately arrived at, which is that the evolution of human consciousness is following a prescribed, scientifically determined path mapped out for us by some unknown genius of the distant past.

I am aware that this is a somewhat controversial statement, one which is no doubt destined to cause something of a stir in the dustier halls of Academia; but on this issue my hand has, in a sense, been forced, in that the established scientific and historical facts – not mine, but the products of the labours of innumerable independent researchers – have consistently pointed toward the very same conclusion. If all my efforts are in reality merely the rantings of a deranged pyramidiot, then doubtless my critics will in due course let me know. In the meantime, however, I am compelled to follow my own instincts, sharpened by personal experience, which tell me that the road to the New Jerusalem does indeed begin at the Giza terminal, and that the individual who designed and built it moved in cosmic circles so vast as to make the twentieth-century social animal's own little world seem like the centre of the dot in the middle.

Now, should it successfully run the gauntlet of the said critics, this conclusion of mine, I suspect, has a very good chance of becoming the title page of a whole new epic story yet to be written; and, of course, if the story so far is anything to judge by, then the resultant sequel will also unfold, chapter and verse, strictly according to the Grand Hermetic Plan.

Indeed it is impossible to conceive of what shape, if any, modern science would be in today had the key to infinity never been cut. The classical convention of $\frac{22}{7}$ is not only a workably close approximation of the true diameter-to-circumference ratio but also – and this is important – from the earliest times it has been instrumental in drawing the attention of the scientist and the mathematician toward the problem of squaring the circle, and so ultimately to the important discovery of the obvious benefits to be derived from the practical applications of the projected value of *pi*.

Consider also the other 'science' we call religion. I think it true to say that every major religion, without exception, contains elements of the supernatural, particularly with regard to the countless numbers of people who have been so profoundly affected by this or that particular code. Religions exist, and have existed since the dawn of recorded history, guiding man's conscience, inspiring his artistic potentialities, raising his consciousness toward the heavens. But then, if the 'signals of Thoth' had never been so resoundingly struck in time, what other forms of belief system would men and women have created for themselves over these millennia?

Without *pi*, therefore, would there still be such a thing as a cathedral, say, or a particle accelerator, a mosque or an electron microscope, a temple or a space shuttle?

Then there are the arts: painting, sculpture, music. We know the great Renaissance masters had knowledge of the old Egyptian 'canon of proportions' and that they applied it to much of their work. Perhaps it is precisely because of their understanding of certain of these esoteric principles of visual harmony, the precise details of which are now lost, or at least hidden, that they were able to achieve such a high degree of artistic expression. As for the world's great composers, is it conceivable that they might have independently found some other artistic means of impressing us all to such dramatic effect had not man's life been so greatly enriched by the knowledge and application of the musical scale?

No. It seems to me, at least, that life on earth without the hermetic code would be overwhelmingly animal, aggressive, 'naturally selective'. You may feel that life is like that now, which indeed it is, to some extent, but eradicate every single trace of Thoth's influence from man's race-memory and you would be left with little more than the cosmic equivalent of a cartload of monkeys.

However, the human being is potentially very different from the animal. If he or she were not, then perhaps the Great Architect himself would have elected to pass this planet by. But this was not the case. The father of Revelation landed and reconnoitred here for a considerable period of time, his express intention being to present mankind with an indelible token of its 'coming of age', a metaphysical key to a completely new and infinitely richer existence.

As we have seen so many times on our musical helter-skelter down through the ages, this key has opened countless doors over literally thousands of years. The story of our evolution, however, as I said, is far from over, and I personally believe we may, in the future, be able to use the same key to unravel many more mysteries. I mean, quite apart from its original intended purpose – that of facilitating the individual evolution of each and every one of us – the theory of transcendental evolution could well have practical applications in the material world, the world of science in particular.

As an outsider, I can only begin to imagine the enormous diffculties encountered by such as the nuclear physicist and the biologist as they each prepare themselves for a final, electrochemical assault on the very portals of inner space. These intricate pursuits of the mind I have barely skipped over, taking snapshots as I passed. One such simple yet very elegant picture which has stuck in my mind happens to be of a biomolecular nature. I will mention it here in the sincere hope that the detail it embodies may positively enhance the scientist's ability to understand what is really going on when, for instance, a deadly virus enters a healthy living cell.

Viruses are actually disease-producing 'particles' which are only capable of multiplication within a host cell. The simplest kind consists of a single helical strand of RNA coated with protein molecules. The main active principle of the particle is the RNA component which, sometimes in concert with trace proteins, enters the cell in one of a variety of ways, where it subsequently disrupts the normal processes of genetic development by using the host's activated amino acids and enzymes to reproduce itself.

A typical simple virus used extensively in biological and biochemical studies is TMV – the tobacco mosaic virus. This particle consists of a single helix of RNA containing some 6400 nucleotides, coated with about 2200 molecules of a single protein. Each of the protein molecules comprises a polypeptide chain of 158 amino acids in a known sequence. Clearly the numbers of nucleotides and protein molecules is virtually an exact repetition, on a higher and more complex scale, of the sixty-four combinations of bases and the twenty-two amino-acid signals, thus indicating that TMV itself is 'hermetically composed' from the top of its head to the tip of its tiny tail. There are, of course, many more of these 'enlightened' denizens of the microcosm which are much more complex in structure and I personally know very little about them, but given all the facts uncovered to date, I think there is good reason for supposing that all of them follow the very same basic evolutionary pattern.

Whether such information could ever be used effectively on a practical level remains to be seen. It is something which would need to be studied in concert by experts in many fields. One would have thought, nonetheless, that the scientific community in general would be greatly assisted in its unswerving quest for a 'theory of everything' – life's purpose included – by a conscious effort on the part of investigators first to attune themselves to the infinite harmony of creation. On a wider scale, of course, we must conclude that a basic grounding in musical theory, both exoteric and esoteric, would do us all the power of good.

Michael Hayes,
Birmingham, September 1993

Selected Bibliography

Bhaktivedanta, A. C. *Bhavagad Gita As It Is*. Collier Books, New York, 1968.

Blavatsky, Helena. *Isis Unveiled*. Theosophical University Press, Pasadena, CA, 1974.

Blavatsky, Helena. *The Secret Doctrine*. Theosophical University Press, Pasadena, CA, 1974.

Boyce, Mary. *Textual Sources for the Study of Zoroastrianism*. Manchester University Press, 1984.

Bunte, Eibert. *Between Stars and Atoms*. Michael Joseph, London, 1962.

Clark, Ronald W. *Einstein, The Life and Times*. Hodder & Stoughton, London, 1984.

Cohen, Jane L. *Buddha*. Macdonald, London, 1970.

Collin, Rodney. *The Theory of Celestial Influence*. Robinson & Watkins, London, 1980.

Crick, Francis. *What Mad Pursuit?* Weidenfeld & Nicolson, London, 1988.

Davidson, D. *The Great Pyramid: Its Divine Message*. Williams & Norgate, London, 1926.

Dodd, C. H. *The Founder of Christianity*. Collins, Glasgow, 1971.

d'Olivet, Fabre. *Golden Verses of Pythagoras*. Thorsons, Wellingborough, 1975.

Donnelly, Ignatius. *Atlantis, the Antediluvian World*. Sidgwick & Jackson, London, 1970.

Feer, Leon. *Samyutta-Nikaya*, vol. 5. Pali Text Society, Oxford, 1929–35.

Gershevitch, I. *The Avestan Hymns to Mithra*, Cambridge University Press, 1959.

Gurdjieff, G. I. *Beelzebub's Tales to His Grandson: An Objective, Impartial Criticism on the Life of Man*. Routledge & Kegan Paul, London, 1950.

Gurdjieff, G. I. *Meetings with Remarkable Men*. Routledge & Kegan Paul, London, 1963.

Gurdjieff, G. I. *Views from the Real World*. Routledge & Kegan Paul, London, 1976.

Gurdjieff, G. I. *Life is real only then, when 'I am'*. Routledge & Kegan Paul, London, 1981.

Hamilton, E. and Cairns, H. *Collected Dialogues of Plato*. Princeton University Press, 1973.

Harris,J. R. *The Legacy of Egypt*. Oxford University Press, 1971.

Hawking, Stephen. *A Brief History of Time*. Bantam, London, 1988.

Huson, Paul. *The Devil's Picture Book*. Abacus, London, 1971.

Jacobi, Jolande. *Paracelsus, Selected Writings*. Routledge & Kegan Paul, London, 1951.

Jung, Carl G. *Memories, Dreams, Reflections*. Fontana, London, 1983.

Lau, D. C. *Tao Te Ching*. Penguin, Harmondsworth, 1963.

Legge, James. *I Ching*. Dover Publications, New York, 1963.

Legge, James. *Shu Ching, Book of History*. Allen & Unwin, London, 1971.

Macgreggor-Mathers, S. L. *Kabbalah Unveiled*. Routledge & Kegan Paul, London, 1971.

Max-Muller, F. *The Laws of Manu*. Motilal Banarsidas, Delhi, 1964.

Melham, Tom. *Mysteries of the Ancient World*. National Geographic Society, Washington, 1979.

Mendelsohn, Kurt. *The Riddle of the Pyramids*. Thames & Hudson, London, 1976.

Mohammed. *The Koran*. Everyman edn. J. M. Dent, London, 1909.

Ouspensky, Piotr D. *In Search of the Miraculous*. Routledge & Kegan Paul, London, 1951.

Shah, Idris. *The Way of the Sufi*. Penguin, Harmondsworth, 1987.

Sharma, R. D. *The Vedic Fundamentals*. Jan Prakashan, Delhi, 1971.

Stewart, Desmond. *The Foreigner*. Hamish Hamilton, London, 1981.

Various contributors. Testaments Old and New; authorized versions.

Waley, Arthur. *Analects of Confucius*. Unwin Hyman, London, 1988.

Wilhelm, Richard. *I Ching*; foreword by C. G. Jung. Routledge & Kegan Paul, London, 1951.

Wilson, Colin. *The Occult*. Granada/Mayflower, London, 1973.

Zaehner, R. C. *The Dawn and Twilight of Zoroastrianism*. Weidenfeld & Nicolson, London, 1961.

Index